ALL NEW 100

MATHS LESSONS

HOMEWORK & ASSESSMENT

YEAR 2

Caroline Clissold

Credits

Author
Caroline Clissold

Editor
Sue Elliott

Series Consultant
Ann Montague-
Smith

Assistant Editors
Aileen Lalor
Victoria Paley

Illustrations
Debbie Clark - Beehive illustration
Jenny Tulip - Beehive illustration

Series Designer
Catherine Mason

Designers
Catherine Mason
Melissa Leeke
Helen Taylor

Text © Caroline Clissold © 2006 Scholastic Ltd

Designed using Adobe InDesign

Published by Scholastic Ltd
Villiers House
Clarendon Avenue
Leamington Spa
Warwickshire CV32 5PR

www.scholastic.co.uk

Printed by Bell and Bain Ltd, Glasgow.

456789   89012345

ACKNOWLEDGEMENTS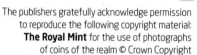

The publishers gratefully acknowledge permission
to reproduce the following copyright material:
The Royal Mint for the use of photographs
of coins of the realm © Crown Copyright

British Library Cataloguing-in-Publication Data
A catalogue record for this book is available from
the British Library.

ISBN 0-439-965-144
ISBN 978-0439-965149

The right of Caroline Clissold to be identified as
the author of this work has been asserted by her
in accordance with the Copyright, Designs and
Patents Act 1988.

Extracts from The National Numeracy Strategy
© Crown copyright. Reproduced under the terms
of HMSO Guidance

Contents

HOMEWORK

ASSESSMENT

Contents

ASSESSMENT

About the series

100 Maths Homework and Assessment Activities offers a complete solution to your planning and resourcing for maths homework and assessment activities. There are seven books in the series, one for each year group from Reception to Year 6.

Each *All New 100 Maths Homework and Assessment Activities* book contains approximately 60 homework activities, with activity sheets to take home, and assessments for each half term, end of term and end of year.

The homework and assessment activities support planning, based on the National Numeracy Strategy's medium-term plans and sample unit plans, but using the language of the learning objectives for that year as they appear in the NNS *Framework for Teaching Mathematics* (DfEE, 1999).

About the homework activities

Each homework activity is presented as a photocopiable page, with some supporting notes for parents and helpers provided underneath the activity. Teacher's notes appear in a grid format for each term at the beginning of each term's activities. There are unit references in the grid, which reference the homework activities to the relevant units in the NNS medium-term plan. Page references are also given that correspond to the relevant activities in the sister book, *All New 100 Maths Lessons Year 2* (Scholastic). This grid is the only place in the book where the objectives and further details about the homework are provided. It is left to your professional judgement as to when exactly the homework is set and followed up. There are homework activities to support each NNS unit, and advice in the grid about managing the homework.

Across the *All New 100 Maths Homework and Assessment* series, the homework activities cover the range of homework types suggested by the National Numeracy Strategy. For Year 2 these include 'Maths to share' activities, and 'Puzzles to do at home':

Maths to share activities encourage the child to discuss the homework task with a parent or carer, and may, for example, involve the home context, or a game to be played with the carer.
Puzzles to do at home are investigations or problem-solving tasks. Again, the parent or carer is encouraged to be involved with the activity, offering support to the child, and discussing the activity and its outcomes with the child.

Using the homework activities

Each homework page includes a 'Helper note', which explains the aim of the homework and how the adult can help to support their child if he or she cannot get started. It is recommended that some form of homework 'diary' be used alongside these activities, through which to establish an effective home–school dialogue about the children's enjoyment and understanding of the homework. You might like to use the homework diary page supplied on page 8 of this book if you currently do not have another resource in use.

Telling the time

(clock)	2:30	(clock)	3:15
(clock)	9:00	(clock)	8:30
(clock)	4:15	(clock)	6:30
(clock)	7:45	(clock)	10:00
(clock)	5:30	(clock)	11:15
(clock)	1:00	(clock)	12:45

Earliest time .... **Latest time**

Dear Helper
This activity will help to develop your child's skills in telling the time. Encourage your child to draw lines to match the times on the analogue clock faces on the left with the correct digital times on the right. If your child struggles, encourage them to focus just on reading the times shown on the analogue clock faces. If they find this activity easy, draw some blank circles on the back of the sheet and ask them to complete the clock faces with their own choice of times, and then to write the corresponding digital labels. Challenge your child to write the digital times shown in order in the box at the bottom of the page.

The teacher's notes grid shown includes:

NNS OBJECTIVES — Teacher's notes

Activity name	Learning objectives	Content of homework	Managing the homework	All New 100 Maths Lessons Year 2	
				NNS	Page
How much?	Find totals, give change, and work out which coins to pay.	**Maths to share** Share a shopping activity.	**Before:** Explain to the children that they will be playing a shopping game that involves buying toys and totalling the amount and giving change. **After:** Review, asking the children to comment on how they got on with their homework. Ask questions such as, *I have one pound. I buy something and am given one coin as change. How much could I have spent?*	4	24
Word search	Use and begin to read the vocabulary related to length, mass and capacity. Use and begin to read the vocabulary related to time.	**Practice** Find vocabulary related to length, mass and capacity in a word search.	**Before:** Tell the children that they will be practising vocabulary related to measures by finding the words in a word search. **After:** Review the activity on an interactive whiteboard or as an OHT, asking some of the children to share the words they found.	5	29
Time for snap!	Use units of time and know the relationship between them (second, minute, hour, day, week).	**Maths to share** Play a matching card game.	**Before:** Explain that this is a 'snap' game to help them revise the relationship between units of time, eg that 60 seconds is one minute. Play the game as a class in two teams. **After:** Recap how many seconds in a minute, minutes in an hour, hours in a day and so on. Observe how quickly the children can recall these facts.	5	32
Describe me	**Use the mathematical names for common 2D and 3D shapes; sort shapes and describe some of their features.**	**Practice** Describe the properties of shapes.	**Before:** Tell the children that they will be looking at properties of shape with their carers and describing them. **After:** Review the activity, asking the children to comment on their homework. Describe some properties of shapes and ask the children to tell you what they are.	6	34
In the bin	**Describe and extend simple number sequences:** count on in twos from zero or any small number.	**Maths to share** Counting in twos game.	**Before:** Explain that the children will be playing a game to practise counting in twos. **After:** Write a number on the board. Ask the children to tell you the next four numbers that come after it if they count in twos. Ask for some numbers that come before it. Repeat with a higher number.	8	39

The teacher's notes

The teacher's notes appear at the start of each term's homework activities. They are presented in a grid format. The grid for the homework activity sets out the following:

● The homework's title.

● The type of homework: 'Maths to share', or 'Puzzles to do at home' for Year 2.

● The NNS Learning objective/s including Key objectives are covered by the homework activity: these are specific to the medium-term plan. Where appropriate, the Key objective/s for that unit have a homework activity. This will help as part of on-going teacher assessment to show how well the children have understood the concepts being taught.

● The content of the homework: this describes briefly the format and content of the activity to help the teacher to make a decision about which homework activity to choose.

● Managing the homework: this section provides two types of help – 'before' and 'after'. The 'before' notes provide suggestions for ways to introduce and explain the homework before the children take it home. These notes might include a brief oral activity to undertake as preparation for the homework. The 'after' notes provide suggestions for how to manage the review of the homework when the children return with it to school. Suggestions include discussing strategies used for solving a problem; comparing solutions; and playing a game as a class.

● NNS unit reference.

● Page link to *All New 100 Maths Lessons Year 2* provides a page reference to the beginning of the unit in this 'sister' book. This will enable practitioners that are using this series to compare what is being taught that week in order to decide which homework to choose and when to send it home.

Developing a homework policy

The homework activities have been written with the DfES 'Homework guidelines' in mind. These can be located in detail on the Standards Site:
www.standards.dfes.gov.uk/homework/goodpractice
The guidelines are a good starting point for planning an effective homework policy. Effective home-school partnership is also vital in ensuring a successful homework policy. The following section outlines some useful starting points.

Encouraging home-school links

An effective working partnership with parents and carers makes a positive impact upon children's attainment in mathematics. The homework activities in this book are part of that partnership. Parents and carers are given guidance on what the homework is about, and on how to be involved with the activity. There are suggestions for helping the children who are struggling with a particular concept, such as ways of counting on or back mentally, and extension ideas for children who would benefit from slightly more advanced work. The homework that is set across the curriculum areas for Year 2 should amount to a total of about one hour a week.

Introduction

The homework diary page, sent home with the homework activity, with opportunities for a response from the parents, can be found on page 8.

The children's assessment activity results can be used in parent or carer discussions with the teacher. The outcomes of the assessment activities, which cover the Key objectives taught that half-term, term or year, will give good evidence for the teacher and parents/carers about how well the child is performing for the year group.

Using the activities with *All New 100 Maths Lessons Year 2*

The activities, both homework and assessment, fit the planning within *All New 100 Maths Lessons Year 2*. As teachers plan their work on a week-by-week basis, so the homework activities can be chosen to fit the appropriate unit of work. They may equally be used alongside the appropriate NNS units, as clearly indicated in the Teacher's notes at the beginning of each term.

For assessment, there are activities to support the 'Assessment lessons' built into the NNS medium-term plan, for example, weeks 7 and 14 in the autumn term of Year 2. The assessment tasks are built around the Key objectives taught during the preceding half-term and all objectives taught are covered in the appropriate assessment. Further information about using the assessment activities can be found on page 84.

Homework diary

Name of activity & date sent home	Child's comments		Parent or helper's comments	Teacher's comments
	Did you like this? Draw a face. ☺ ☺ ☹ a lot a little not much	How much did you learn? Draw a face. ☺ ☺ ☹ a lot a little not much		

ALL NEW 100 MATHS HOMEWORK AND ASSESSMENT · YEAR 2

www.scholastic.co.uk

NNS OBJECTIVES ▭ Teacher's notes

Activity name	Learning objectives	Content of homework	Managing the homework	All New 100 Maths Lessons Year 2	
				NNS	Page
Number line	**Describe and extend simple number sequences: count on or back in ones or tens, from any two-digit number.**	**Practice** Make sequences of numbers by writing a starting number on the board and asking children to continue the sequence.	**Before:** Tell the children that they wil be practising sequencing work. **After:** Review the activity, inviting children to demonstrate their work.	1	8
Combining cards	Know what each number in a two-digit number represents.	**Practice** Use partitioning cards to mentally combine and write the number sentence.	**Before:** Explain that the children will be practising combining tens and ones. **After:** Review the activity, inviting children to demonstrate their work. Hold up two and three digit numbers and ask them to write number sentences.	2	12
Arrow sentences	Use the +, – and = signs to record mental additions and subtractions in a number sentence and recognise the use of a symbol such as ■ or ▲.	**Practice** Use addition and subtraction to complete number sentences.	**Before:** Explain that they will need to choose numbers to make addition and subtraction arrow sentences. You will need to fill in numbers for each child/group to use before copying and distributing this activity. **After:** Review, asking the children to give examples of their work. Put ? + ? = 10 + 2 and ask for possible answers.	2	14
The name game	**Count, read write and order whole numbers to at least 100** in figures and in words.	**Investigation** Make up numbers from a selection of digit cards and record them as words and numerals.	**Before:** Explain that the children will be practising work on number names. **After:** Review the activity, inviting children to tell everyone the highest/lowest/most numbers they found.	3	18
Get some help!	**Choose and use appropriate operations and efficient calculation strategies to solve problems.**	**Maths to share** Make up problems for a helper to answer.	**Before:** Explain that this homework needs to be done with a helper. The children need to make up problems using the information given. **After:** Ask the children to share the problems they made up with the rest of the class and talk about the different ways that they and their helper solved them.	3	21
Toy shopping	Recognise all coins and begin to use £.p notation for money.	**Practice** Use a range of coins to make different totals.	**Before:** Tell the children that they will be practising work in money values and coins. **After:** Review the activity, asking some of the children to show examples of their work during the main part of the lesson.	4	24

NNS OBJECTIVES 🗋 Teacher's notes

Activity name	Learning objectives	Content of homework	Managing the homework	All New 100 Maths Lessons Year 2	
				NNS	Page
How much?	Find totals, give change, and work out which coins to pay.	**Maths to share** Share a shopping activity.	**Before:** Explain to the children that they will be playing a shopping game that involves buying toys and totalling the amount and giving change. **After:** Review, asking the children to comment on how they got on with their homework. Ask questions such as, *I have one pound. I buy something and am given one coin as change. How much could i have spent?*	4	24
Word search	Use and begin to read the vocabulary related to length, mass and capacity. Use and begin to read the vocabulary related to time.	**Practice** Find vocabulary related to length, mass and capacity in a word search.	**Before:** Tell the children that they will be practising vocabulary related to measures by finding the words in a word search. **After:** Review the activity on an interactive whiteboard or as an OHT, asking some of the children to share the words they found.	5	29
Time for snap!	Use units of time and know the relationship between them (second, minute, hour, day, week).	**Maths to share** Play a matching card game.	**Before:** Explain that this is a 'snap' game to help them revise the relationship between units of time, eg that 60 seconds is one minute. Play the game as a class in two teams. **After:** Recap how many seconds in a minute, minutes in an hour, hours in a day and so on. Observe how quickly the children can recall these facts	5	32
Describe me	**Use the mathematical names for common 2D and 3D shapes; sort shapes and describe some of their features.**	**Practice** Describe the properties of shapes.	**Before:** Tell the children that they will be looking at properties of shape with their carers and describing them. **After:** Review the activity, asking the children to comment on their homework. Describe some properties of shapes and ask the children to tell you what they are.	6	34
In the bin	**Describe and extend simple number sequences:** count on in twos from zero or any small number.	**Maths to share** Counting in twos game.	**Before:** Explain that the children will be playing a game to practise counting in twos. **After:** Write a number on the board. Ask the children to tell you the next four numbers that come after it if they count in twos. Ask for some numbers that come before it. Repeat with a higher number.	8	39

Activity name	Learning objectives	Content of homework	Managing the homework	All New 100 Maths Lessons Year 2	
				NNS	Page
Race along the track	Recognise odd and even numbers to at least 30.	**Maths to share** Odds and Evens game.	**Before:** Explain that the children will be playing a game to practise odd and even numbers. **After:** Play the game in two teams. Invite children to pick two digit cards and make two different numbers. Write these on the board, asking whether they are odd or even and which would be the best to use depending on where they are on the track.	8	39
Up the ladder!	**Count, read, write and order whole numbers to at least 100; know what each digit represents (including zero as a place holder).**	**Practice** Generate and write down own numbers, then order them from smallest to largest.	**Before:** Explain that the children will be making two-digit numbers to order. Take them through the activity explaining how to make up their own numbers and what to do with them. **After:** Draw a ladder on the board. Ask the children to suggest sensible positions to write various two digit numbers on the ladder, explaining their choices. Ask if they thought carefully about the positions in their homework.	9	47
Beat the clock!	**Know by heart all addition and subtraction facts for each number to at least ten.**	**Practice** Time the children as they complete number sentences using + and -.	**Before:** Explain that the children will be practising the addition and subtraction facts to at least ten, and that they will be timed to see how quickly they can recall these facts. **After:** Select volunteers to have a go at a speed challenge, where you call out the part of the fact and the children call out or write the missing part.	9	48
Loopy lines	Begin to understand division as repeated subtraction.	**Practice** Show multiplication and its inverse by making jumps along a number line.	**Before:** Explain that this activity focuses on multiplication as repeated addition and division as repeated subtraction. Before copying the sheet, fill in the boxes according to each child's ability. **After:** Work through a few of the children's calculations. Through discussion and self assessment, assess how they felt they did. Do they understand that division is the opposite operation to multiplication and is repeated subtraction?	10	54
Double trouble maze	Use known number facts and place value to carry out mentally simple multiplications and divisions.	**Practice** Find your way through a doubling maze.	**Before:** Demonstrate how to go around the maze by correctly doubling the number at each junction. **After:** Use a correctly completed maze and copy it on to acetate, put it on the OHP and work through it with the class.	11	58

NNS OBJECTIVES 🖵 Teacher's notes

Activity name	Learning objectives	Content of homework	Managing the homework	All New 100 Maths Lessons Year 2	
				NNS	Page
Quarter mastery	Find one half and one quarter of shapes.	**Investigation** Use a paper folding activity to find quarters of shapes.	**Before:** Tell the children that this activity involves finding halves and then quarters of different shpaes by folding them. **After:** Discuss which shapes could be folded into quarters and which could not and why.	11	60
Percy's hungry	Find one half and one quarter of numbers.	**Maths to share** Play a game to halve and quarter numbers.	**Before:** Explain that the children will be playing a game that will require them to halve and quarter numbers. Fill in the number spinners with appropriate numbers for individual children/ability groups before copying and distributing the sheet. **After:** Find out whether the children can correctly work out ½ and ¼ of the numbers that you put on the spinners.	11	60
Reading scales	**Read a simple scale to the nearest labelled division, including using a ruler to draw and measure lines to the nearest centimetre.**	**Maths to share** Draw and measure length, mass and capacity.	**Before:** Carefully explain the homework, stressing that the children must only do the practical measuring with an adult. **After:** Discuss why the words *between, exactly, just under, nearly* were necessary and how they helped them to read the scales. Find out if the children were able to do the practical activities and how accurate they thought they were.	12	62
Telling the time	Read the time to the hour, half hour or quarter hour on analogue and a 12-hour digital clock.	**Maths to share** Find and record times on clocks.	**Before:** Tell the children that they will be working out the time on analogue clock faces and matching it to digital displays. **After:** Check the answers together. Find out if any of the children did the ordering and, if so, ask for their results. If not, do the activity together as a class.	12	65
Shape puzzle	Solve mathematical problems or puzzles. Suggest simple extensions by asking *What if...?*	**Maths to share** Shape puzzle.	**Before:** Decide which values you want the shapes to be, filling in a few of the totals to make the puzzle possible to solve. Differentiate the activity by varying the values of the shapes. **After:** Make an OHT of the sheet. Discuss with the children how they solved the homework. Ask questions such as: *Which row column shall we look at first? Why?*	13	70

Name	Date

Number line

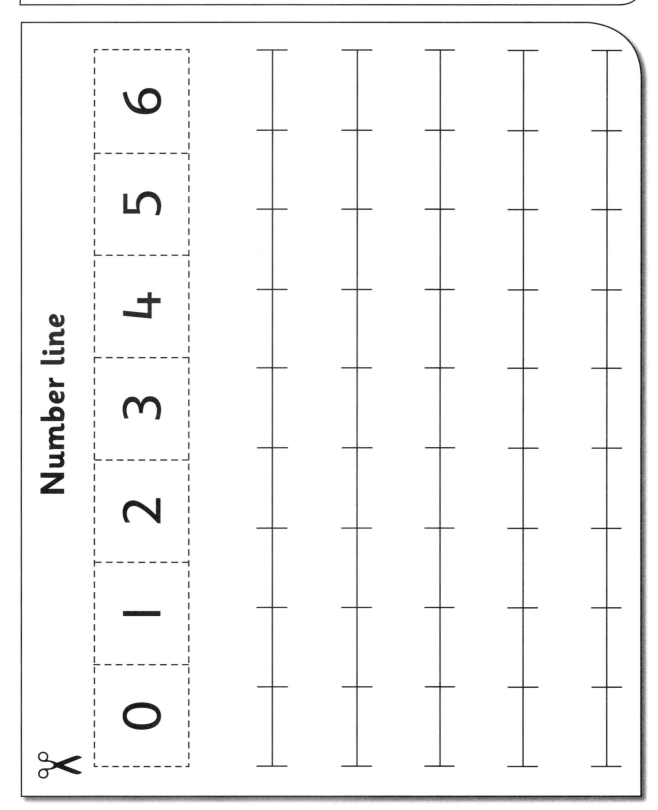

0 1 2 3 4 5 6

Dear Helper
This activity will help your child to count on and back in ones. Help your child to cut out the small number cards, then ask them to pick two cards and put them together to make a two-digit number, for example, 3 and 2 to make 32. Write the number in the middle of the number line. Ask your child to fill in the rest of the number line, counting up and down in ones from that number. If your child finds this difficult, write a two-digit number at the beginning of the number line, then ask them to count up from that number. If your child wants a challenge, ask them to count on and back in twos.

PHOTOCOPIABLE

Name   Date

Combining cards

◖ Put the tens and ones cards together to make as many new numbers as you can. Record your work. For example:

| 4 0 | | 1 | | 4 1 | |

$$40 + 1 = 41$$

| 5 | | 2 | ✂ |

| 7 | | 1 | ✂ |

| 4   0 | | 1   0 | ✂ |

| 7   0 | | 3   0 | ✂ |

Dear Helper
This activity will support the work that your child has been doing on partitioning. Help them to cut out the partitioning cards. Invite them to put one ten and one unit card together to make a new number, for example, 40 and 1 to make 41. Challenge them to make as many different two-digit numbers as they can, using different combinations of cards. Encourage them to record their work, for example, 40 + 1 = 41. If they need a challenge, ask them to make hundreds cards as well.

PHOTOCOPIABLE

www.scholastic.co.uk

Name   Date

Arrow sentences

■ Choose two numbers and make an arrow sentence.

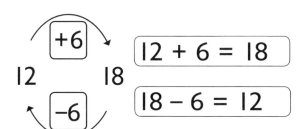

$$12 + 6 = 18$$

$$18 - 6 = 12$$

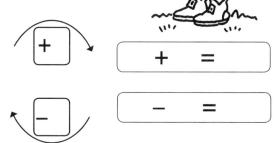

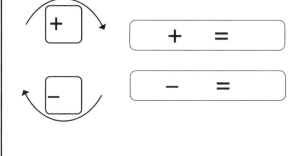

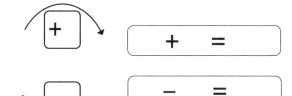

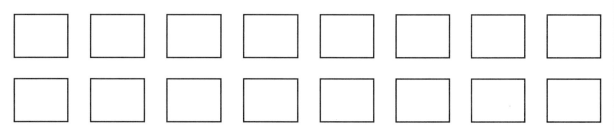

Dear Helper
This activity will help to reinforce your child's mental addition and subtraction skills. The numbers in the boxes above have been chosen specifically for them. Encourage them to choose two numbers for each arrow sentence, then help them to complete each arrow sentence by working out and writing down which number they will need to add and subtract each time. One example has been done for you.

Name

Date

The name game

How many new two-digit numbers can you find in 15 minutes? Write each number, and its name in words, in the space below.
For example, '47, forty seven'.

| 2 | 3 | 4 | 7 | 8 |

Helpful words	
twenty	two
thirty	three
forty	four
seventy	seven
eighty	eight

47, forty seven	

Dear Helper

This activity will consolidate your child's knowledge of number names. Explain that you would like them to make two-digit numbers from the numbers at the top of the page. When they have made a new number, ask them to write it down in numerals and in words. After 15 minutes, ask them to stop and count how many numbers they have made. If they have difficulty, ask them to write single digits and words. If they want a challenge, ask them to make up and name three-digit numbers.

www.scholastic.co.uk

Name

Date

Get some help!

For example:

14   6

How many more?

My mum has 14 pairs of shoes. I have 6 pairs. How many more pairs has she got than me?

If I count from your 6 to your mum's 14, I get a difference of 8: 7, 8, 9, 10, 11, 12, 13, 14.

Facts

My word problem

My Helper's answer

14   8

How many more?

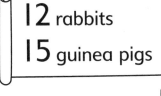

23 dogs were black

12 dogs were white

18 apples

8 pears

12 rabbits

15 guinea pigs

50 sweets

60 chews

Dear Helper

Invite your child to use the facts above as starting points for making up word problems for you to solve. Explain how you solved the problem and/or ask for your child's help. When you have solved each problem, ask them if they can think of another way to work it out.

Name   Date

Toy shopping

25p I used:
20p and 5p

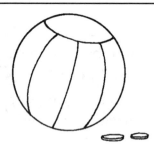

11p I used:

30p I used:

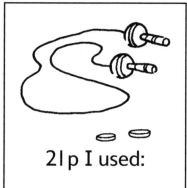

21p I used:

32p I used:

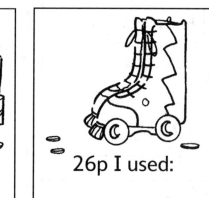

26p I used:

28p I used:

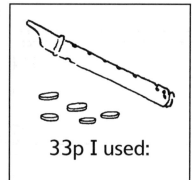

33p I used:

42p I used:

Dear Helper
This activity will provide opportunities for your child to practise their coin work. Provide your child with several 1p, 2p, 5p, 10p and 20p coins. Ask your child to look at the price underneath each toy and put the correct coins on to each picture to make up the price of the toy. Challenge them to use the fewest coins possible to make up the price, and to tell you what they are doing. Encourage them to record which coins they used. The first example has been done for you.

PHOTOCOPIABLE

How much?

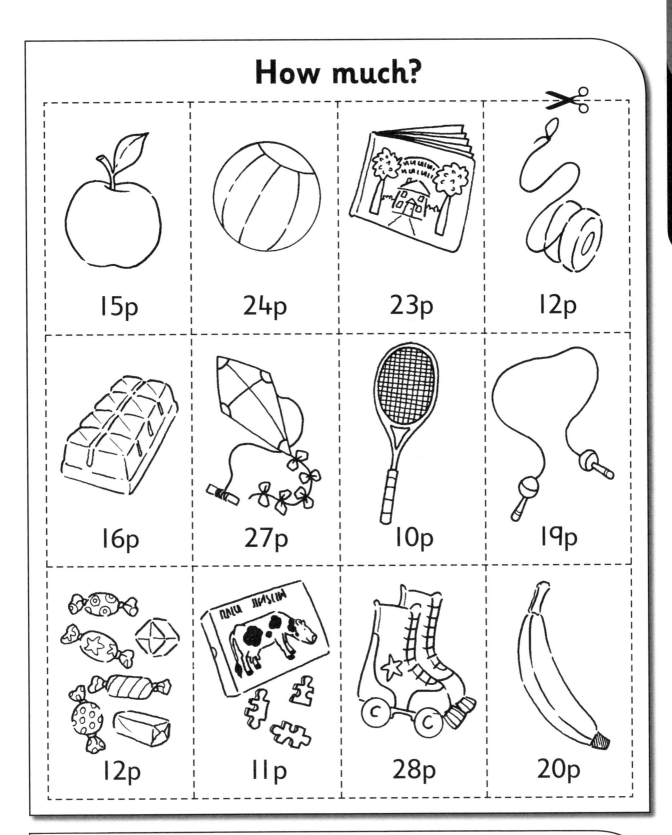

15p	24p	23p	12p
16p	27p	10p	19p
12p	11p	28p	20p

Dear Helper

This activity provides practise in working out totals and giving change. Cut out the cards and provide your child with several 1p, 2p, 5p, 10p, 20p and 50p coins. Allocate the roles 'shopper' and 'shopkeeper'. The shopper should choose two cards and give them to the shopkeeper together with 50p. The shopkeeper should work out the total cost of the two items, and give the shopper their change. If the total is more than 50p, the shopper should choose different cards. If your child has difficulty, use one card and 30p. For more of a challenge, use three cards and £1.

PHOTOCOPIABLE

Name
Date

Word search

■ Find these words in the word search below.

centimetre	container	full	light
litre	metre	scales	second
tall	week	year	

l	m	e	t	r	e	e	s	x	z
i	h	j	k	l	m	r	c	n	c
t	w	e	e	k	h	t	a	y	o
r	t	a	l	l	w	e	l	r	n
e	q	w	f	g	h	m	e	d	t
a	t	f	u	l	l	i	s	n	a
n	h	b	v	c	x	t	z	o	i
o	g	y	e	a	r	n	u	c	n
o	i	d	f	g	h	e	k	e	e
u	l	y	t	r	e	c	w	s	r

Dear Helper

This word search contains words relating to measures. Encourage your child to find the words in the box above and to draw a line through each one as they find it. The words are arranged horizontally and vertically, forwards and backwards. If your child has difficulty, help them to find the first letter. If your child would like a challenge, do not show them the word list until they have found all the words.

Time for snap!

60 seconds	I minute	I minute
60 seconds	I hour	60 seconds
24 hours	I day	I hour
7 days	I week	60 minutes
2 weeks	I fortnight	I day
52 weeks	I year	24 hours
120 seconds	2 minutes	7 days
I week	120 seconds	2 hours

Dear Helper

This game will help to consolidate your child's learning on units of time. Cut out, shuffle and deal the cards out equally. Place them face down in front of you and take turns to turn a card over from your own pile. If a card shows the same amount of time as the previous card, for example, '1 minute' and '60 seconds', both players should shout 'Snap!'. The first to shout collects the cards. If your child has difficulty, write out the equivalent times on paper for them to refer to. For a challenge, time the children to see how quickly they can link the cards together to form a 'domino' chain.

Name _____   Date _____

Describe me

1. Description

Sides: _____

Corners: _____

Symmetrical: _____

Name: _____

2. Description

Sides: _____

Corners: _____

Symmetrical: _____

Name: _____

3. Description

Sides: _____

Corners: _____

Symmetrical: _____

Name: _____

4. Description

Sides: _____

Corners: _____

Symmetrical: _____

Name: _____

5. Description

Sides: _____

Corners: _____

Symmetrical: _____

Name: _____

6. Description

Sides: _____

Corners: _____

Symmetrical: _____

Name: _____

Dear Helper

This activity will reinforce work on properties of different shapes. Invite your child to talk about each shape in turn. Encourage them to fill in all the spaces. Give prompts and scribe the name of the shape if your child is having difficulty. If they need a challenge, ask them to focus on two shapes that have the same name and note their similarities and differences.

Name

Date

In the bin

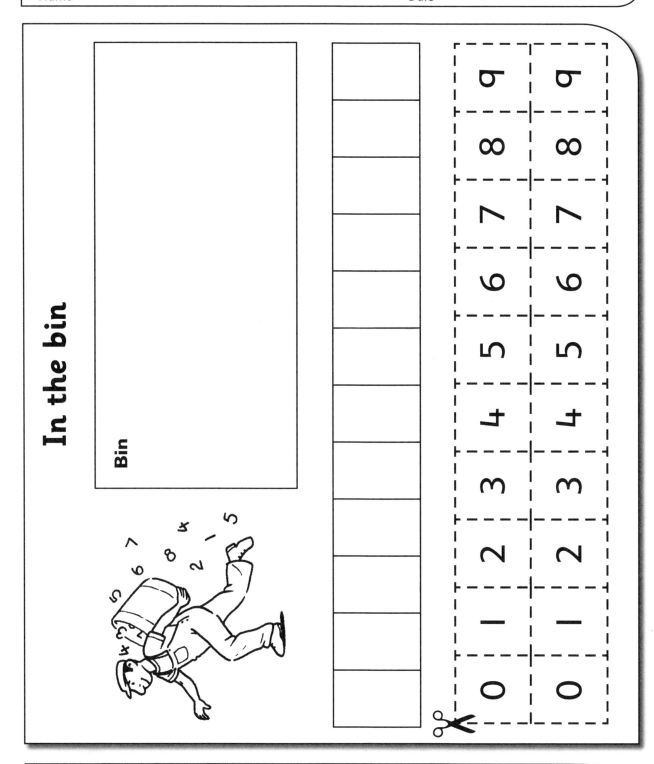

Bin

Dear Helper

This game will help your child to count on in twos. Cut out the number cards and place them face down. Players take it in turns to turn over two number cards to make a two-digit number. The first player writes their two-digit number in the first box. Players afterwards should write their two-digit number in the box that follows the sequence of counting on in twos from the first number. Each time a number in the sequence is made, a point is scored. If a number can not be made in the sequence, it should be written in the 'bin'. For numbers which fit the sequence but there are not enough boxes allocated, they should write this number on a seperate piece of paper and award themselves a point. The player with the most points is the winner. If your child is having difficulty, make the first number one or two. If they would like a challenge, ask them to make three-digit numbers.

Race along the track

■ You each need number cards 1–9. One of you needs to be 'odd' and the other 'even'.

■ Turn the cards face down on the table.

■ Take it in turns to pick two cards and make a two-digit number, eg if you are 'even' and pick 3 and 4 you can make 34. You need to write 34 in the starter box that says 'Even'. On your next turn, if you can make an even number you write it in the first cross.

■ If you are 'odd', do the same but on the octagon line. If you cannot make your type of number, you miss a go.

■ The player who gets to the end of their track first is the winner.

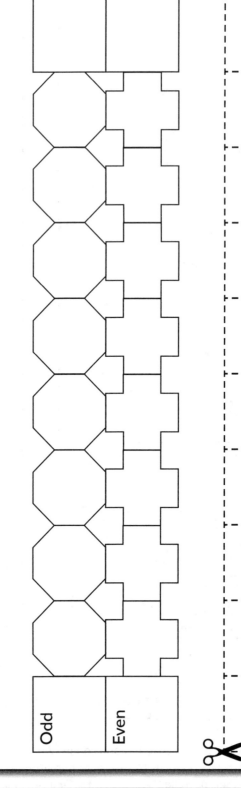

Odd

Even

0 1 2 3 4 5 6 7 8 9

Dear Helper

This game will help to reinforce the work the child has been doing with odd and even numbers. Help your child to cut out the number cards and go through the instructions carefully with them. If they have difficulty, write down a list of numbers that odd and even numbers must end with.

If they want a challenge, ask your child to make up a new set of rules for this game – it must still be about odd and even numbers!

Name

Date

Up the ladder!

- Use the numbers at the bottom of the page to make two-digit numbers.

- Write your numbers in this box:

0	1	2	3	4
5	6	7	8	9

- Now order them on the ladder, smallest at the bottom

Dear Helper

This activity will help your child to practise ordering numbers up to 100. Cut out the number cards and invite your child to use them to make ten two-digit numbers, and write them in the space provided. Now encourage your child to put the numbers in order on the ladder, with the smallest number at the bottom and the largest number at the top. If your child is having difficulty, use numbers to 20. If your child needs a challenge, time them.

Name   Date

Beat the clock!

$6 +$ ☐ $= 7$ $5 +$ ☐ $= 7$ $2 +$ ☐ $= 7$

$4 +$ ☐ $= 7$ $2 +$ ☐ $= 5$ $0 +$ ☐ $= 5$

$3 +$ ☐ $= 5$ $5 +$ ☐ $= 5$ ☐ $+ 9 = 10$

☐ $+ 3 = 10$ ☐ $+ 6 = 10$ ☐ $+ 2 = 10$

$9 -$ ☐ $= 7$ $10 -$ ☐ $= 7$ $10 -$ ☐ $= 6$

$8 -$ ☐ $= 7$ $7 -$ ☐ $= 5$ $8 -$ ☐ $= 5$

$9 -$ ☐ $= 5$ $5 -$ ☐ $= 5$ ☐ $- 9 = 0$

☐ $- 3 = 5$ ☐ $- 6 = 4$ ☐ $- 2 = 7$

Dear Helper
Your child has been learning by heart addition and subtraction facts for numbers to at least ten. Give your child ten minutes to complete as many sums as possible. If your child has difficulty, allow them to use counters to help them and do not time them. Reduce the time for children who would like a challenge.

PHOTOCOPIABLE

www.scholastic.co.uk

Loopy lines

- Complete the number lines by drawing loops along the lines to show the multiplication or division in each box.

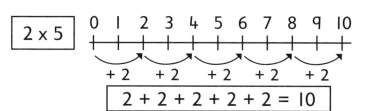

2×5

0 1 2 3 4 5 6 7 8 9 10

+ 2   + 2   + 2   + 2   + 2

$$2 + 2 + 2 + 2 + 2 = 10$$

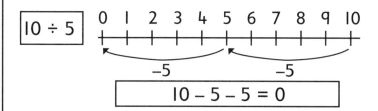

$10 \div 5$

0 1 2 3 4 5 6 7 8 9 10

−5   −5

$$10 - 5 - 5 = 0$$

0 1 2 3 4 5 6 7 8 9 10 11 12 13 14 15 16 17 18 19 20

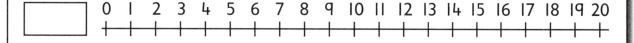

0 1 2 3 4 5 6 7 8 9 10 11 12 13 14 15 16 17 18 19 20

0 1 2 3 4 5 6 7 8 9 10 11 12 13 14 15 16 17 18 19 20

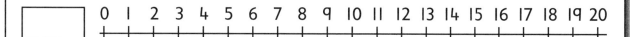

0 1 2 3 4 5 6 7 8 9 10 11 12 13 14 15 16 17 18 19 20

0 1 2 3 4 5 6 7 8 9 10 11 12 13 14 15 16 17 18 19 20

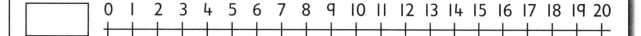

Dear Helper

Your child has been learning that division is repeated subtraction. Remind them that this is the opposite of multiplication, which is repeated addition. Work through the examples below with your child. Encourage your child to write the repeated addition or subtraction, and the answer, underneath each number line. The multiplications have been filled in according to your child's confidence with division.

Double trouble maze

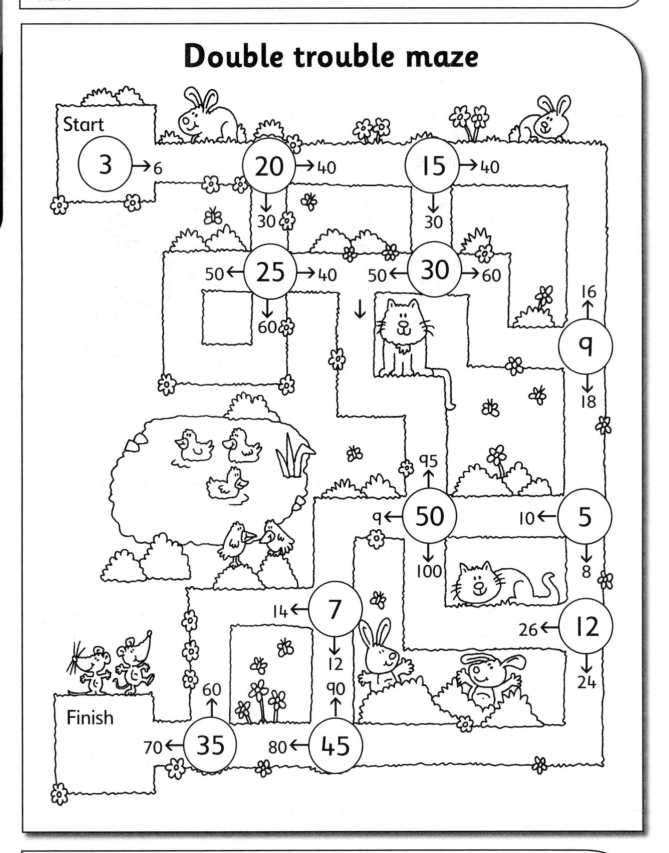

Dear Helper

This activity will help your child to practise doubling numbers. To travel through the maze, your child must correctly double each of the numbers in a circle and then follow the appropriate arrow. Ask your child to mark out their route and afterwards check they have gone the correct way. If your child has difficulty, ask them to add the number twice using partitioning strategies where appropriate. For a challenge, ask them to make up their own 'Double trouble maze' using different numbers.

PHOTOCOPIABLE

www.scholastic.co.uk

Name	Date

Quarter mastery

- Cut out each shape and fold it into four quaters.

- Unfold the shape and mark along the fold lines with a coloured pen.

- Which shapes have four equal sections?

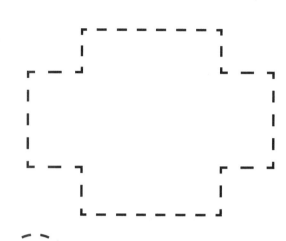

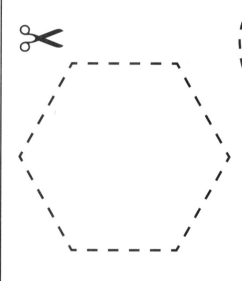

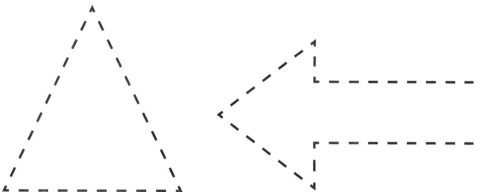

Dear Helper
This activity will consolidate the work that your child has been doing on fractions and shapes. Help your child to carefully cut out each shape, then challenge them to fold each shape into quarters. Ask your child to unfold their shapes and mark along the fold lines. On a separate piece of paper, encourage your child to record which of the shapes are formed from four quaters.

www.scholastic.co.uk   ALL NEW 100 MATHS HOMEWORK AND ASSESSMENT · YEAR 2

Name _____   Date _____

Percy's hungry

- Cut out each spinner. Put the sharp end of a pencil through a paper clip and then through the middle of the spinner.

- Spin the paper clip around the fraction spinner.

- Spin the paper clip around the number spinner.

- Work out the answer to the fraction sum and place that amount of counters on Percy's tummy.

Number Spinner

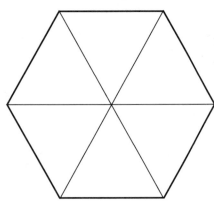

Fraction Spinner

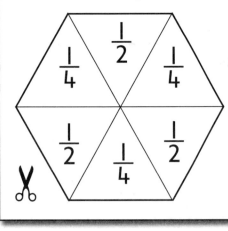

Dear Helper

This game will help your child to work out halves and quarters of numbers. The numbers on the number spinner have been specifically chosen for your child. You will need some buttons or counters to represent food for Percy. Encourage your child to flick the paperclip around the fraction spinner to choose a fraction, and around the number spinner to choose a number. Help your child to work out the answer depending on the numbers spun. So, for example, if they spin a quarter and 12, then they must work out quarter of 12, and count out that many counters to put on to Percy's tummy. How much food can your child feed Percy in five minutes?

Name	Date

Reading scales

◀ Measure along the line and record your answer in the box.

This line is: [ ]

◀ Measure flour or sugar on to some scales so that they show the same weight as the scales on this sheet?

This weight is: [ ]

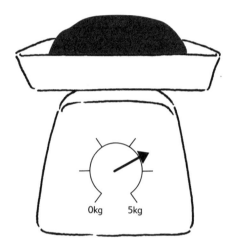

0kg   5kg

◀ Can you measure water into a measuring jug so that it looks the same as the jug on this sheet?

This capacity is: [ ]

2 litres

0

Dear Helper
This activity will reinforce the work that your child has been doing on reading measures. Work through the questions together, letting your child practically measure out the amounts for capacity and weight if possible, and encourage them to write their answers in the boxes. Please provide a ruler for your child, as well as suitable scales and a measuring jug. If your child has difficulty, guide them with your finger for the ruler work and mark on the intervals on the scales and jug.

PHOTOCOPIABLE

Name _____   Date _____

Telling the time

  2:30

  9:00

  4:15

  7:45

  5:30

  1:00

3:15

8:30

6:30

10:00

11:15

12:45

Earliest time   **Latest time**

Dear Helper

This activity will help to develop your child's skills in telling the time. Encourage your child to draw lines to match the times on the analogue clock faces on the left with the correct digital times on the right. If your child struggles, encourage them to focus just on reading the times shown on the analogue clock faces. If they find this activity easy, draw some blank circles on the back of the sheet and ask them to complete the clock faces with their own choice of times, and then to write the corresponding digital labels. Challenge your child to write the digital times shown in order in the box at the bottom of the page.

Shape puzzle

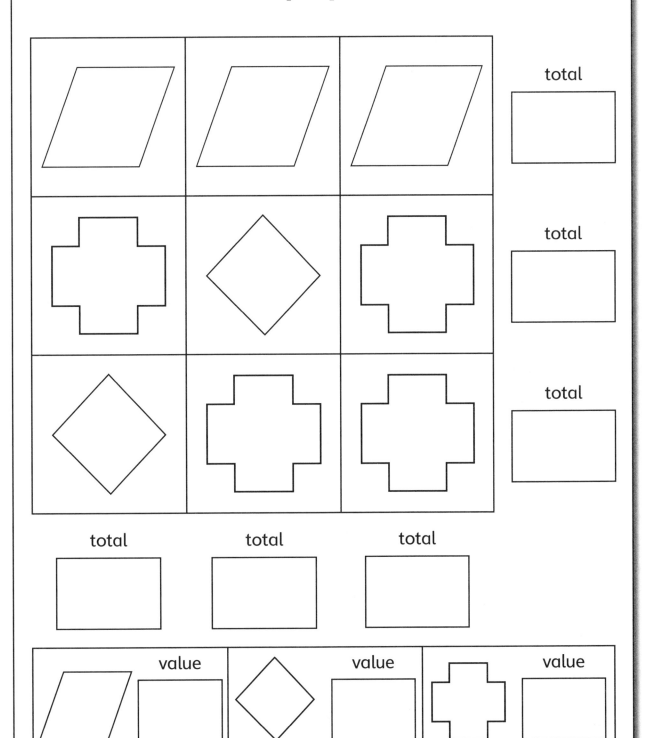

www.scholastic.co.uk

PHOTOCOPIABLE

Dear Helper
Explain to your child that each shape above represents a different number. Your child's teacher will already have filled in some shapes appropriate to your child's ability. Using these totals, help your child to work out the value of each shape, and then to work out the remaining totals.

NNS OBJECTIVES ◻ Teacher's notes

Activity name	Learning objectives	Content of homework	Managing the homework	All New 100 Maths Lessons Year 2	
				NNS	Page
Spotting multiples	Begin to recognise two-digit multiples of two, five or ten.	**Investigation** Ring multiples of two, five and ten.	**Before:** Explain that the homework focuses on multiples of two, five and ten. Using a swinging pendulum, or something similar, rehearse counting in multiples of these numbers. **After:** Correct the activity as a class. Ask: *How do you know that four is a multiple of two only, 15 is a multiple of five only and ten is a multiple of both two and ten?*	1	78
Dots before your eyes	Count reliably up to 100 objects by grouping them.	**Practice** Practise counting by grouping.	**Before:** Demonstrate how to group and count items on the board. **After:** Ask some of the children to demonstrate what they did using an OHT of the homework sheet. Ask: *When is it best to group things into ten when we count them. Why? When we haven't got a group of ten what other groups could we use?*	1	78
Spider charts	**Know by heart facts for the two- and ten-multiplication tables.**	**Maths to share** Practise two and ten times-tables and division facts using spider charts.	**Before:** Tell the children that they will be practising their two and ten times-tables and will need to ask their helpers to time them. **After:** Ask whether anyone felt they answered their homework facts quickly using thumbs up/down signalling. Use large versions of the spider charts to practice the tables.	2	82
Rounding up	Use and begin to read the vocabulary of estimation and approximation.	**Practice** Estimate answers to addition calculations before working them out.	**Before:** Fill in numbers for each child/group before copying and distributing the sheets. Work through examples together, encouraging the children to estimate by rounding. **After:** Ask the children to give examples of their work. Discuss rounding each number to a multiple of ten and adding them to give a basic estimate. Look for strategies they used to total the numbers.	2	84
Totals to ten	**Use knowledge that addition can be done in any order to do mental calculations more efficiently.**	**Investigation** Add three small numbers, two of which should total ten. Explain the addition strategy to a helper.	**Before:** Explain that the children will be practising to add three numbers using the strategy finding two that make ten first. **After:** Invite the children to tell everyone the highest/lowest/most numbers they found. Ask the children which pairs total ten or a multiple of ten. Establish that adding ten to a number is easier than adding others.	3	90

Activity name	Learning objectives	Content of homework	Managing the homework	All New 100 Maths Lessons Year 2	
				NNS	Page
Partitioning and recombining	Use knowledge that addition can be done in any order to do mental calculations more efficiently.	**Practice** Add from a choice of two-digit numbers by partitioning.	**Before:** Model an example from the sheet, asking the children to suggest which numbers to choose, how to partition, add and then recombine. **After:** If the children found this difficult encourage them to put forward a simpler method. Extend by asking them to partition higher numbers. Explain that it is just as simple to add larger numbers in this way.	3	90
Making problems	Choose and use appropriate operations and efficient calculation strategies to solve problems.	**Maths to share** Make up problems for a helper to answer.	**Before:** Explain that this homework needs to be done with a helper. Demonstrate how to make up problems using the information given on the sheet. **After:** Ask the children to share the problems that they made up and to talk about the different ways that they and their helper solved them.	4	95
All the same value	Choose and use appropriate operations and efficient calculation strategies to solve problems.	**Investigation** Find different multiples of ten that total two pounds.	**Before:** Model an example: the total cost is £1, all the toys cost the same and must be a multiple of ten. There are two toys, so how much could they cost? Work through all the possibilities. **After:** Ask for all the possible answers. *Could the toys cost 25p each? Why not? Could they cost 80p each? Why not?*	4	95
Measures	Read a simple scale to the nearest labelled division.	**Practice** Read scales to work out measurements.	**Before:** Tell the children that their homework is to practise reading scales either exactly or to the nearest measurement. **After:** Photocopy a homework sheet on to acetate and work through it with the children.	5	101
Where is the arrow?	Use mathematical vocabulary to describe position, direction and movement.	**Practice** Match words to directions.	**Before:** Show the children the activity sheet and read through the positional and directional language together. **After:** Review the activity, asking some of the children to share examples of their work.	6	109

35

NNS OBJECTIVES ⬜ Teacher's notes

Activity name	Learning objectives	Content of homework	Managing the homework	All New 100 Maths Lessons Year 2	
				NNS	Page
Stepping stones	**Describe and extend simple number sequences:** count on in steps of three, four or five to at least 30, from and back to zero, or any given small number.	**Practice** Count on and back in steps of three, four and five.	**Before:** Explain to the children that they will be practising counting in threes, fours and fives. Fill in the step number and a few numbers on the line to show the children what you want them to count in and the number range. **After:** Repeat the activity with the class using a blank acetate. Ask how the children knew where each number should go.	8	112
Right or wrong?	Investigate a general statement about familiar numbers or shapes by finding examples to satisfy it.	**Investigation** Decide whether general statements about numbers and shapes are right or wrong.	**Before:** Explain that the children need to work out whether the statements on the sheet are right or wrong and then write down their reason. Everyone should be able to do the first four examples. More able children may also like to try the last two. **After:** Take each question in turn and ask the children what they thought. Invite as many reasons as possible.	8	115
Fill your ladder	**Count, read, write and order whole numbers to at least 100.**	**Maths to share** Generate own numbers and order these from smallest to highest.	**Before:** Model this game. When you make each two-digit number, show both possibilities and ask which would be best. For example, Which would fit best – 34 or 43? It may not matter at first, but as the rungs fill up it will. Show the children how the numbers are ordered from smallest to biggest **After:** Revisit the game as a whole-class activity.	9	120
Grouping	**Understand the operation of multiplication as repeated addition or as describing an array** and begin to understand division as repeated subtraction.	**Practice** Interpret division statements in numbers and symbols in order to calculate the answers.	**Before:** Fill in the numbers according to the children's ability. Use numbers to 20 with less able children, to 30 with the main group and to 50 for more able children. Work through a couple of examples. **After:** Determine whether the children understand grouping by working out such calculations as 10 ÷ 5 and 30 ÷ 10.	10	126
Investigate these facts	**Choose and use an appropriate operation and efficient calculation strategies to solve problems.**	**Investigation** Work out multiplication and division problems.	**Before:** Fill in the boxes according to the children's ability. Use numbers to 20 for less able children, to 30 for the main group and to 50 for more able children. **After:** Determine whether the children understand that division is the opposite operation to multiplication and can be seen as repeated subtraction.	10	128

Activity name	Learning objectives	Content of homework	Managing the homework	All New 100 Maths Lessons Year 2	
				NNS	Page
Halves and quarters	Begin to recognise and find one half and one quarter of shapes and small numbers of objects.	**Maths to share** Play a game to work out halves and quarters.	**Before:** Ensure that the children understand what halves and quarters are in the context of a small number of objects. **After:** Repeat the game, playing against the rest of the class. Ask the children how they find a quarter or a half. Do they partition or keep the number whole, do they use halving facts that they have learned in school?	11	132
Time crossword	Read the time. Begin to use the vocabulary relating to time.	**Maths to share** Complete a crossword to reinforce the vocabulary of time.	**Before:** Discuss the meaning of the words in the box, asking for possible answers to the clues. You may wish to fill in some of the letters in each word, to make it easier for the children. **After:** Say each solution word and ask the children to make up a clue of their own to demonstrate their understanding of the meanings of the words.	11	134
Favourite colours	Solve a given problem by sorting, classifying and organising information in simple ways. Discuss and explain results.	**Maths to share** List the facts that you can find from a pictogram.	**Before:** Tell the children that they are going to list as many facts as they can from the pictogram on the homework sheet. Explain that they can use numbers instead of words, for example, *five like red.* **After:** Invite the children to share some of the facts that they found.	12	136
Sorting it out	Solve a given problem by sorting, classifying and organising information in simple ways. Discuss and explain results.	**Maths to share** Solve a problem using data from a list and make up block graph.	**Before:** Remind the children about block graphs and pictograms. Show them the homework on an OHT and ask what labels need to be written on. Discuss how you can show how many children like each colour paint. **After:** Look at everyone's results and ask questions: *How many children were in the class? Which was the most popular colour paint?*	12	136

Name _____   Date _____

Spotting multiples

■ Put a ring around the multiples of 2 on this line:

1 2 3 4 5 6 7 8 9 10 11 12 13 14 15 16 17 18 19 20

■ Put a ring around the multiples of 5 on this line:

7 8 9 10 11 12 13 14 15 16 17 18 19 20 21 22 23 24 25

■ Put a ring around the multiples of 10 on this line:

9 10 11 12 13 14 15 16 17 18 19 20 21 22 23 24

■ Put a ring around the multiples of 2 and a square around the multiples of 5 on this line:

31 32 33 34 35 36 37 38 39 40 41 42 43 44 45 46 47 48 49 50

■ Put a ring around the multiples of 5 and a square around the multiples of 10 on this line:

47 48 49 50 51 52 53 54 55 56 57 58 59 60 61 62

■ Which of these are multiples of 2? Put a ring around them:

23 44 12 67 43 78 14 16 60 38 21 83 97

■ How do you know which numbers are multiples of 2? Write down your answer on the back of the sheet.

Dear Helper

This activity will help your child to recognise multiples of two, five and ten. Ask your child to follow the instructions above each number line. If they have difficulty, concentrate on multiples of one number only. To challenge your child, see if they can make up number lines for three-digit numbers.

Name	Date

Dots before your eyes

Count these dots by drawing hoops around each group of 10.

How many dots are there?

35

Count these dots by drawing hoops around each group of 10.

How many dots are there?

Count these dots by drawing hoops around each group of 5.

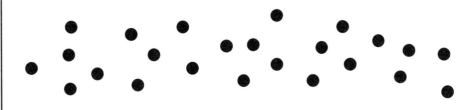

How many dots are there?

Count these dots by drawing hoops around each group of 2.

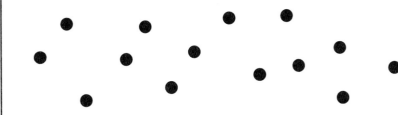

How many dots are there?

Dear Helper
This activity encourages your child to group numbers in order to help them count more efficiently. Read the instructions for counting each set of dots, then encourage your child to fill in the correct totals in the boxes. The first example has been done for you. If your child has difficulty, encourage them to mark dots as they count and then loop them together. For a challenge, ask your child to draw 12 dots on the back of the sheet and find all the possible ways of grouping.

PHOTOCOPIABLE

www.scholastic.co.uk

ALL NEW 100 MATHS HOMEWORK AND ASSESSMENT • YEAR 2

Name _____   Date _____

Spider charts

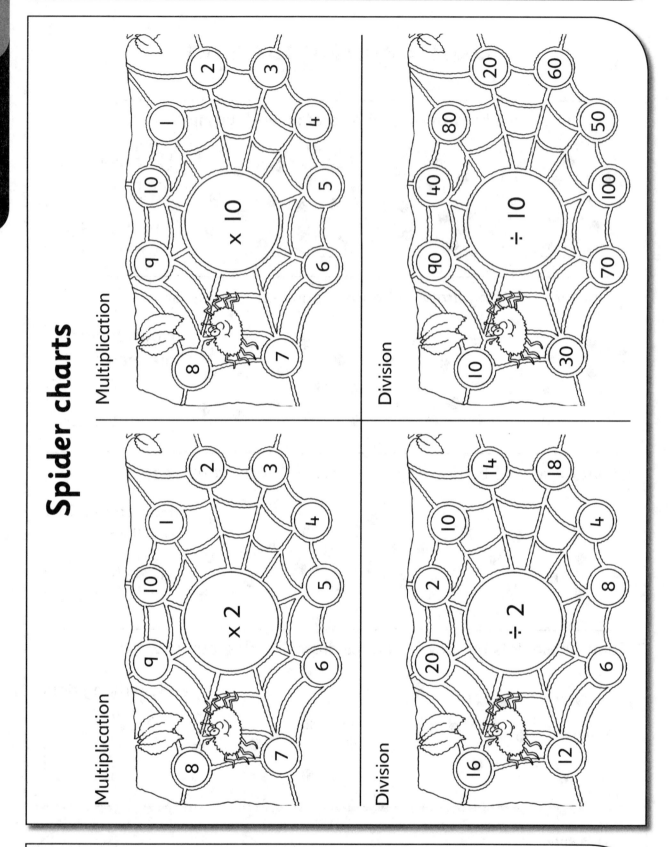

Multiplication — × 10

Multiplication — × 2

Division — ÷ 10

Division — ÷ 2

Dear Helper

These spider charts will help your child to practise their two- and ten-times tables. For the multiplication charts, point to a number on the outside of the chart and challenge your child to multiply it by two (or ten, depending on which chart you are using) and call out the answer. Time your child to see how quickly they can work out the answer. Do the same with the division charts.

PHOTOCOPIABLE

www.scholastic.co.uk

Name   Date

Rounding up

My numbers are:

My estimate is:

My answer is:

How I worked out the answer:

My numbers are:

My estimate is:

My answer is:

How I worked out the answer:

My numbers are:

My estimate is:

My answer is:

How I worked out the answer:

Dear Helper

Your child has been learning how to estimate an answer to a calculation before working it out, by using a rounding strategy. Ask your child to choose three different numbers from the boxes at the top of the page. (The numbers in the boxes have been chosen to match your child's abilities.) Challenge your child to estimate what the answer will be when the three numbers are addded together, and to write the estimate in the box, before working out the correct answer. Encourage them to write down the strategy they used. Repeat the activity using different numbers.

Name

Date

Totals to ten

2	3	4	6	7	8
12	13	14	16	17	18

◼ Choose three numbers to add together. Make sure two of the numbers total ten and add these together first.

◼ Next add on the third number. Explain your work to your helper.

Numbers chosen: 3 7 12	Numbers totalling 10: 3 and 7	Addition: $3 + 7 = 10$ $12 + 10 = 22$
Numbers chosen:	Numbers totalling 10:	Addition:
Numbers chosen:	Numbers totalling 10:	Addition:
Numbers chosen:	Numbers totalling 10:	Addition:
Numbers chosen:	Numbers totalling 10:	Addition:

◼ Now make up some more on the back of this sheet.

Dear Helper
Your child has been learning how to look for numbers that total ten. Encourage them to explain their strategy to you. Now encourage them to use the strategy to add three numbers from the top of the page. If your child has difficulty, tell them to add the single digits only. If they would like a challenge, ask them to add the two-digit numbers only.

PHOTOCOPIABLE

www.scholastic.co.uk

Partitioning and recombining

12	14	15	16	17	18
24	26	27	35	32	33

◀ Choose two numbers to add together. Add them by 'partitioning and recombining'. Explain your work to your Helper.

For example:

Numbers chosen: 24 and 35	Partitioning: 20 + 4 + 30 + 5	Addition: 50 + 9 Recombining: 59
Numbers chosen:	Partitioning:	Addition: Recombining:
Numbers chosen:	Partitioning:	Addition: Recombining:
Numbers chosen:	Partitioning:	Addition: Recombining:
Numbers chosen:	Partitioning:	Addition: Recombining:

◀ Now make up some more on the back of this sheet.

Dear Helper
Your child has been learning to add by partitioning numbers into tens and units. For example, 14 is 10 + 4 and 35 is 30 + 5; 14 + 35 = 10 + 4 + 30 + 5 = 40 + 9 = 49. Let your child explain this partitioning and recombining strategy to you. If your child has difficulty, ask them to use numbers with unit digits less than five. To challenge your child, ask them to use numbers with digits over five.

Name   Date

Making problems

◀ Use the number facts on this sheet to make up problems for your Helper to answer.

£5

£4.50

My problem:

The answer:

£1.50

2

My problem:

The answer:

£1.50

£5

My problem:

The answer:

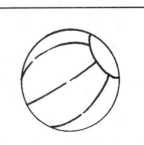

75p

10

My problem:

The answer:

Dear Helper
Encourage your child to use the facts on this sheet to make up some problems for you to answer.
For example: *I would like to buy two books, each costing £1.50. How much money will I need?* Extend
the problem by asking: *How much change will I get if I pay with £5?* If your child has difficulty, write the
problems for them and let them use real coins and notes. For a challenge, encourage them to make
up some more problems with their own amounts of money.

PHOTOCOPIABLE

www.scholastic.co.uk

Name

Date

All the same value

■ These three toys all cost the same price. The price is a multiple of ten. The total cost of the three toys is less than £2. What could the value of each toy be? Write your answers in the box below.

 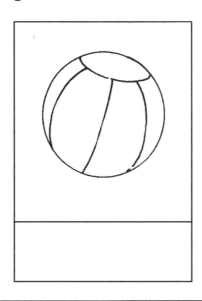 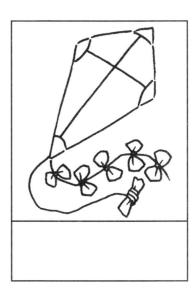

My answers:

■ What could the value of each toy be if the total was a multiple of five and less than £1?

My answers:

Dear Helper
Your child has been investigating number problems and learning that investigations often result in more than one answer. For their homework, your child should find and record all possible answers to the questions above. Encourage your child to be systematic in their approach.

Name _____   Date _____

Measures

◀ Record the correct measurements on the lines below.

The apples weigh

_____ kg.

The bananas weigh just

over _____ kg.

The string is

_____ cm long.

There is just over _____

litres of liquid in the jug.

There is just under _____

litres of liquid in the jug.

Dear Helper

Please help your child to read the scales to work out the answers. Encourage your child to write the answers in the spaces provided. If your child has difficulty, count along each scale with them in the appropriate intervals. For a challenge, encourage them to try and give an accurate reading.

Name

Date

Where is the arrow?

◀ Decide which direction the arrows are pointing from the words listed below.

◀ Write your answer beneath each box.

clockwise	anti-clockwise	quarter turn
in front	right angle	higher
lower	behind	beside

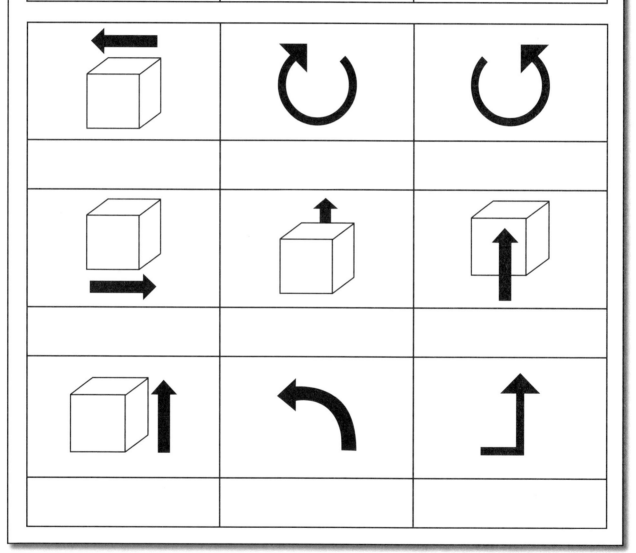

Dear Helper

This activity will help consolidate your child's knowledge on position and direction. Discuss the position or direction of the arrow in each picture, and help your child to find the correct word from those listed. Write the answer below each picture. If your child has difficulty, use practical apparatus like a teddy and a box and place the teddy in the positions on the sheet. For a challenge, ask them to think of other positions and direction words and draw arrows to show them.

PHOTOCOPIABLE

Name   Date

Stepping stones

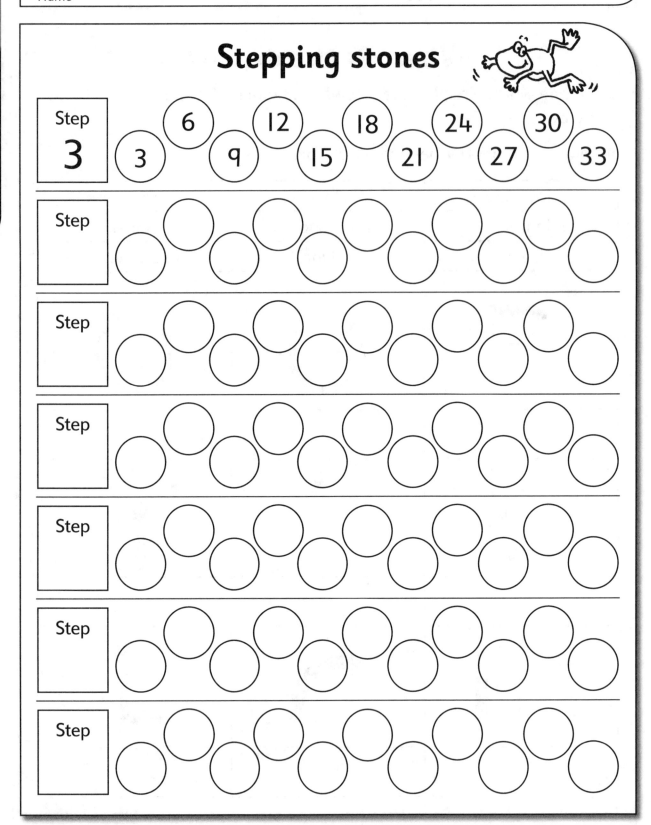

| Step 3 | 3 | 6 | 9 | 12 | 15 | 18 | 21 | 24 | 27 | 30 | 33 |

Step

Step

Step

Step

Step

Step

Dear Helper

Your child has been learning to count in steps of three, four and five, from and back to small numbers. Encourage your child to look at the starting numbers and the step numbers that have already been filled in, and then to complete the number lines counting in steps of that number. The starting numbers and step numbers have been filled in according to your child's ability. An example has been done for you.

Name	Date

Right or wrong?

🔲 Read the statements below and decide if they are right or wrong.

Statement 1

This is a cylinder.

This is right/wrong because

Statement 2

21 is an odd number.

This is right/wrong because

Statement 3

I can make 10p using 1p, 2p, 5p and 10p coins in just three different ways.

This is right/wrong because

Dear Helper
Your child has been investigating statements and proving that they are right or wrong. Encourage your child to work through the statements below, explaining why they think each one is right or wrong. If your child's explanation is quite lengthy, and they are having difficulty, please help them to write it down. If your child finds the first four statements quite easy to solve, challenge them to have a go at the last two, which are slightly more difficult.

Name _____   Date _____

Fill your ladder

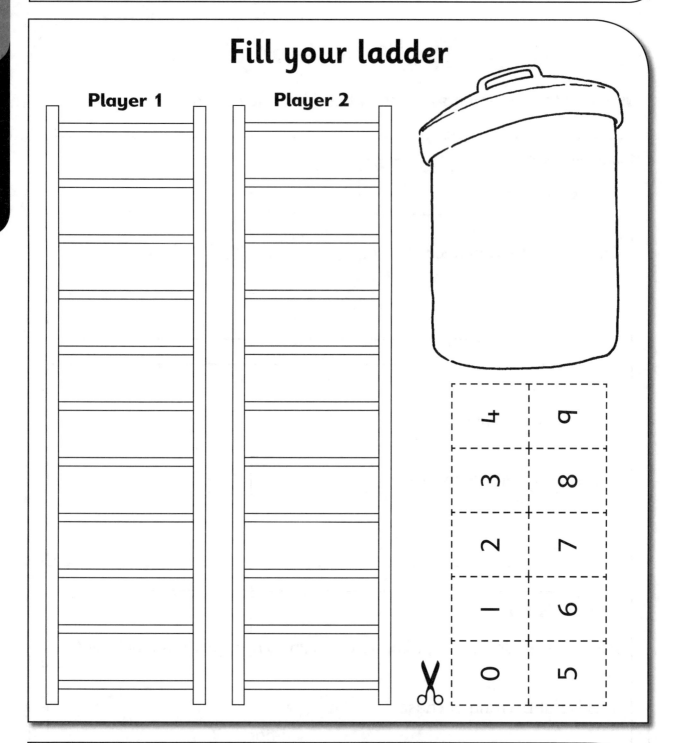

Player 1   **Player 2**

Number cards: 4 9 3 8 1 2 7 6 0 5

Dear Helper

This game will help your child to prastice ordering numbers up to 100. Cut out the 0-9 number cards. The first player should choose two cards to make a two-digit number. Depending on whether the number is high or low, the player should write that number on an appropriate rung on their ladder. For example, a 4 and a 9, could make 49 or 94. You may choose to write 49 in the middle of the ladder, or 94 at the top. There are only ten rungs, so choose your rung carefully. The next player should then take their turn. Choose which way around to use your numbers depending on the space left on your ladder. As the rungs fill up, your number may not fit on so write that number in the bin and let the next player take their turn. The winner is the first player to fill their ladder. If your child has difficulty, make numbers to 20, by choosing the 1 or the 2 as the tens number. For a challenge, encourage them to make a new 20 rung ladder and order all the numbers you both made onto it.

Name Date

Grouping

- Work out the following division facts. Use the grouping method to help you.

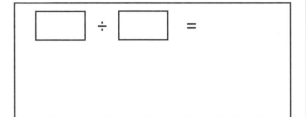

8 ÷ 2 -2 -2 -2 -2 8 6 4 2 0 We can take 4 lots of 2 away from 8, so 8 ÷ 2 = 4	☐ ÷ ☐ =
☐ ÷ ☐ =	☐ ÷ ☐ =
☐ ÷ ☐ =	☐ ÷ ☐ =
☐ ÷ ☐ =	☐ ÷ ☐ =

- Make up some more of your own on the back of this sheet for your Helper to solve.

Dear Helper

This activity will help your child to practise the division work that they have been doing in class. The numbers have been specially chosen for your child. Work through each example together, using the space available in each box to write down the calculations. Encourage your child to find the answers by grouping. For example: 8 ÷ 2. To work this out your child will need to find out how many groups of 2 there are in 8. They can do this by taking groups of 2 away from 8 (see the first example). If your child has difficulty, ask them just to partition numbers into tens and ones. For a challenge, ask your child to use pairs of two-digit numbers to make up their own calculations.

Name _____   Date _____

Investigate these facts

A car has 4 wheels.

How many wheels are there on ☐ cars?

_____

Show how you worked this out.

Sara had ☐ cm of sticky tape.

She wanted to cut it into ☐ cm lengths.

How many lengths can she cut? _____

Show how you worked this out.

Jo had a ☐ m length of rope.

Sam had ☐ as much.

How much did Sam have? _____

How much did Jo and Sam have altogether?

_____

Show how you worked this out.

Emma has ☐ stamps.

Ravi has ☐ stamps for every one of Emma's.

How many stamps does Ravi have?

_____

Show how you worked this out.

Dear Helper

This activity will help your child to practise problem solving that involves multiplication and division. The numbers have been specially chosen to match your child's ability. Please provide help to read the problems if necessary. Your child may find it helpful to use practical objects, such as pennies or pieces of pasta, for this activity. If your child needs a challenge, ask them to make up similar questions to for you to answer.

Halves and quarters

Amount	$\frac{1}{2}$	$\frac{1}{4}$	Points
8	4	2	6
15	No	No	0
18	9	No	2

🐾 Drop a handful of counters onto a table. Count how many there are.

🐾 Can you halve this number? Can you quarter this number? Award yourself the correct number of points as shown above.

Child

Amount	$\frac{1}{2}$	$\frac{1}{4}$	Points

Helper

Amount	$\frac{1}{2}$	$\frac{1}{4}$	Points

Dear Helper
This game will help to consolidate the work on fractions that your child has been doing in class. You will need lots of counters. Encourage your child to start the game by picking up a handful of counters and dropping them on to the table. Can they divide them into half? If they can, they score two points. Can they divide them into quarters? If so, they score four points. For each turn, fill in one row of the table, writing the amount of counters dropped, what their half or quater value is, or *No* if the fraction is not possible, and the points scored. The first player to score 20 points is the winner. For a challenge, use more counters. If your child has difficulty, play the game concentrating on halves only.

Name _____ Date _____

Time crossword

Words

morning

minute

fortnight

analogue

after

watch

afternoon

seconds

digital

early

evenings

late

Clues Across

2. The time of day when we get up.

4. Not before.

5. After lunch and before tea.

7. Not late.

9. Opposite of early.

10. The time of the day when we go to bed.

11. The type of watch that has just numbers.

Clues Down

1. Every two weeks.

3. We use this to tell the time.

4. The type of watch that has hands.

6. There are 60 of these in a minute.

8. There are 60 of these in an hour.

Dear Helper

This activity will help your child to practise some of the vocabulary of time that they have been learning in class. If your child would like a challenge, hide the box with words to choose from. If they need more support, help them by filling in two or three of the answers.

Name _____ Date _____

Favourite colours

◢ Write as many sentences as you can based on the data below. If you need more space, use the back of this sheet.

◢ Each smiley face stands for one child.

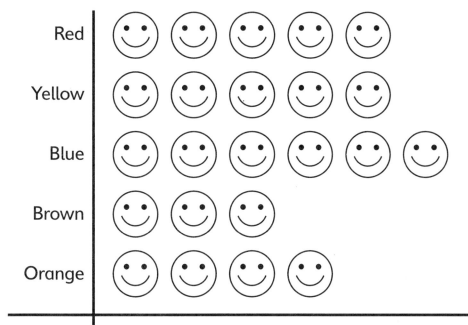

Red

Yellow

Blue

Brown

Orange

Number of children

One more child likes orange than likes brown.

Blue is the most popular colour.

_____

_____

_____

_____

Dear Helper
This activity will consolidate the work on data handling that your child has been doing at school. Ask your child to look at the pictogram above. Each smiley face represents one child. Encourage your child, using the space beneath the pictogram, to write down as many things as possible about what the data is telling them. Two examples have been given.

Name _____ Date _____

Sorting it out

Problem

I would like to order some paint for art, but I need you to help me decide which three colours to buy. I asked the class to tell me their favourite colours, and this is what they said:

2 liked black	3 liked orange	4 liked red
1 liked green	10 liked yellow	6 liked white

◀ Which are the three most popular colours? Add the information to the block graph to find out.

Number of children

Colours

PHOTOCOPIABLE

Activity name	Learning objectives	Content of homework	Managing the homework	All New 100 Maths Lessons Year 2	
				NNS	Page
Odds and evens	Describe and extend simple number sequences (including odd/even numbers).	**Maths to share** Odds and evens game. Make sure you attach a paper clip to the game.	**Before:** Play the game with the children as a whole class to show them what to do. **After:** Spin some pairs of numbers, ask the children if they are odd or even. Total them, ask if the answer is odd or even. Bring to their attention the fact that when adding two odd numbers or two even numbers the answer is even.	1	144
The ordering game	Count, read, write and order numbers to at least 100.	**Maths to share** Ordering game.	**Before:** Explain to the children that they will be practising ordering numbers and need to ask their helper to play this game with them. Demonstrate the game from the homework sheet. **After:** Ask the children to tell you how they made the biggest numbers? Which number did they put in the units position?	2	150
Inversions	Understand that subtraction is the inverse of addition.	**Practice** Matching card game for inversions.	**Before:** Demonstrate exactly what to do using enlarged cards from a copy of the homework sheet. **After:** Play the game as a class. Put an addition sentence on the board. Ask: *What other addition can be made. What two subtractions can be made?*	2	150
Split the number	Use known number facts and place value to add/subtract mentally.	**Practice** Use the partitioning method to add two numbers.	**Before:** Make differentiated versions of this sheet by filling in the four remaining numbers on the sheet. Demonstrate how to complete the activity. **After:** Invite children to demonstrate some of their work. Ask questions such as: *Which number did you choose to partition? Why? How did you find your answer?*	3	159
Which method?	Use known number facts and place value to add/subtract mentally.	**Practice** Which strategy is the best to use to solve a calculation?	**Before:** Make differentiated versions of this sheet by filling in the calculations according to the children's ability. Discuss possible strategies; near doubles, counting on, partitioning, rounding and number bonds. Demonstrate how to complete the activity. **After:** Discuss each strategy and ask the children to suggest an appropriate calculation to go with each one.	3	159
Pence to pounds	Recognise all coins and begin to use £.p notation for money.	**Maths to share** Changing pence into pound notation.	**Before:** Visit pence to pounds and pence notation with the class before you give out this homework. **After:** Write some amounts of pence on the board eg 345p and invite children to write them in pounds and pence. Ask them to explain how they worked the additions out.	4	166

NNS OBJECTIVES ☐ Teacher's notes

Activity name	Learning objectives	Content of homework	Managing the homework	All New 100 Maths Lessons Year 2	
				NNS	Page
What a problem!	Use mental addition, and subtraction, simple multiplication and division to solve simple word problems involving numbers in 'real life', money or measures, using one or two steps. Explain how the problem was solved.	**Maths to share** Money problem solving.	**Before:** Differentiate the sheets by filling in the amounts of money appropriate to the individual ability of the children. **After:** Check the children's work with them. Ask children how they worked out their solutions. Which strategies did they use to work out the change – did they count on for example?	4	166
Measure it	**Read a simple scale to the nearest labelled division.**	**Practice** Reading scales.	**Before:** Work through examples of reading scales on the OHP with an acetate copy. **After:** Put the acetate on the OHP and invite children to show how they read the scales and to give their answers.	5	176
Draw the measures	**Read a simple scale to the nearest labelled division.**	**Practice** Drawing scales.	**Before:** Put an acetate copy of the homework on the OHP and work through some examples **After:** Put the acetate on the OHP and invite children to draw the amounts required on the weighing equipment. Ask how they knew the answer.	5	176
Position, direction, movement	**Use mathematical vocabulary to describe position, direction and movement.**	**Practice** Sorting vocabulary words.	**Before:** This homework concentrates on vocabulary related to position, direction and movement. The children have to put the vocabulary into appropriate boxes, one headed position, a second direction and a third movement. **After:** Review as a class. Draw the three 'boxes' on the board. Call out the words and target children to say where they go. Encourage the children to try to make up a sentence using each word, to make sure they have understood it properly.	6	180
Give us a clue!	**Use mathematical names for common 2D and 3D shapes; sort shapes and describe some of their features.**	**Maths to share** Shape matching game.	**Before:** Show the homework page and go through several examples. **After:** Review the homework asking the children to share their answers. Give other clues for these shapes to check that they know the important properties that they have learnt. Give clues that could be applicable to two shapes and ask the difference between them.	6	180

NNS OBJECTIVES ⌨ Teacher's notes

Activity name	Learning objectives	Content of homework	Managing the homework	All New 100 Maths Lessons Year 2	
				NNS	Page
Snaky stripes	Count on in steps of three, four or five to at least 30, from and back to zero, then from and back to any given small number.	**Maths to share** Missing number activity.	**Before:** Write appropriate step sizes and start numbers for each ability group as in the example. You may wish to give additional number clues in some cases. **After:** Using an OHT of the sheet, invite some children to share their work. Ask the children whether the number lines are correct and how they know.	8	186
How many ways?	Solve mathematical problems or puzzles, recognise simple patterns and relationships, generalise and predict. Explain how problem was solved, orally and where appropriate, in writing.	**Maths to share** Making totals from random number cards. Make all numbers to 20 (can include doubling).	**Before:** Fill in the numbers you want the children to make. Multiples of three, four and/ or five will be useful to elicit times table facts. **After:** Using an OHT of the sheet, invite some children to share their work. Ask the others to add their own ideas; encourage them to suggest any operations that have not yet been used.	8	186
Bridging ten	Bridging through ten or 20 then adjusting.	Play a game that involves adding numbers by bridging through ten or 20.	**Before:** Tell the children that they will be practising adding a near multiple of ten and adjusting. Play the game as a class. **After:** Show a copy of the gameboard, give the children a two-digit number eg 48. Say: *Show me how you would add nine? How would you add 11?*	9	191
Doubles and halves	**Know and use halving as the inverse of doubling.**	**Practice** Doubling and halving.	**Before:** Fill in appropriate numbers on the sheet if you wish to differentiate the activity. Write a mixture of instructions, some in words (double/halve) and others with signs and numbers ($\times 2/\div 2$). **After:** Ask some children to explain what they did. Ask such questions as: *How did they double a number? Did they know, or did they partition, or did they count on?* Find out whether they were able to do it independently.	10	195

NNS OBJECTIVES — Teacher's notes

Activity name	Learning objectives	Content of homework	Managing the homework	All New 100 Maths Lessons Year 2	
				NNS	Page
Which coins?	Recognise all coins and begin to use £.p. notation for money (for example know that £4.65 indicates £4 and 65p).	**Investigation** Matching real coins to labels. Making up amounts with a pound coin and one or two others and recording eg £1 + 20p + 2p = £1.22.	**Before:** Fill in appropriate numbers on the sheet according to the children's ability. **After:** Ask some children to explain, using examples from their work, what they did. Ask such questions as: *How did you know that was the fewest number of coins? If there hadn't been 20p, what else could you have used?* Find out whether they were able to do it independently, and whether they used the least possible number of coins.	10	198
Equivalents	Begin to recognise that two halves or four quarters make one whole and that two quarters and one half are equivalent.	**Maths to share** Matching fraction cards that are equivalent.	**Before:** Explain the homework, using an OHT copy of the sheet. **After:** Help the children to mark their own work, using the OHT as your example. Ask: *How many quarters make a whole? How many quarters make a half? If we have ½ and ¼ what fraction is that?*	11	202
Fraction problems	**Choose and use appropriate operations and efficient calculation strategies to solve problems.**	**Maths to share** Fraction problems involving different operations.	**Before:** Fill in appropriate numbers to differentiate the sheets. **After:** Go through the homework with each group, so they can mark their own work. Ask questions such as: *What did you need to find out? What fraction were you trying to find? How did you work it out? Does your answer seem right?*	11	205
Can you find my partner?	Suggest suitable units to estimate or measure time.	**Maths to share** Matching game.	**Before:** Model how to play the game about times of the year. **After:** Hold up the cards and ask the children to think of an answer. They explain their thinking.	12	209
Match the time	Read time to the hour, half hour or quarter hour on an analogue clock and a 12-hour digital clock.	**Maths to share** Snap for clock picture and digital time.	**Before:** Model how to play the game . **After:** Hold up the clock faces and ask the children to write down the digital time and explain their answer.	12	211
Faulty graph	Solve a given problem by sorting information in simple ways, such as: lists; tables; pictograms; block graphs.	**Maths to share** Identify and correct seven mistakes in a block graph.	**Before:** Show the children an acetate of the faulty graph with seven mistakes for them to find; ask for examples. Explain that th ey should find as many mistakes as they can, and correct them. **After:** Show the acetate again, ask for volunteers to come and correct a mistake, explaining why it is wrong. Assess their adeptness at doing this. Invite other children to share information that they wrote down from the corrected graph.	13	215

Odds and evens

Dear Helper

This game will help your child to recognise odd and even numbers. You will each need a different coloured counter to place on the 'Start'. Take turns to spin a number on each spinner. Add the two numbers together. If your number is odd, move on to the next white circle. If it is even, move on to the next black circle. Continue the game in this way. The first to the 'Finish' is the winner. If your child has difficulty, use one spinner only and identify whether the number landed on is odd or even. For a challenge, spin the two-digit spinner twice and add those numbers.

Name

Date

The ordering game

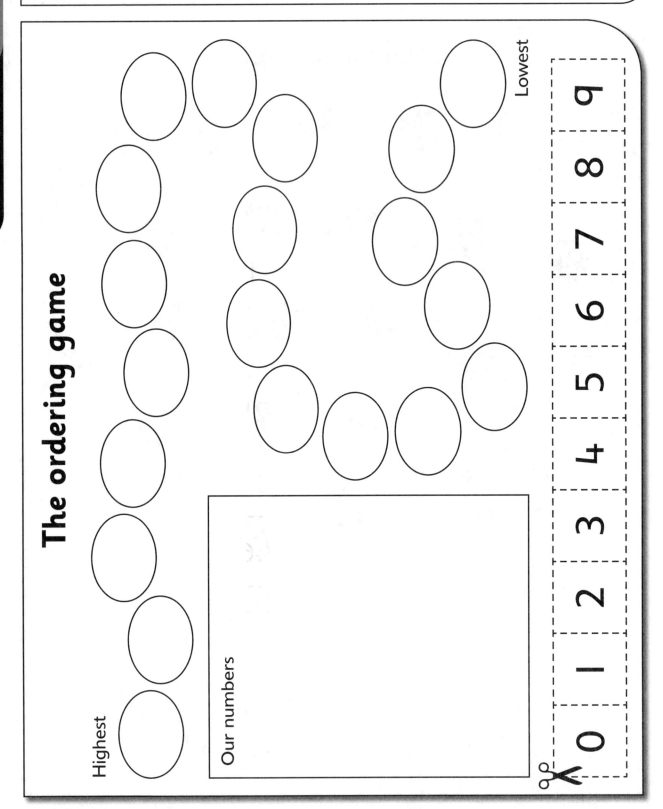

Highest

Our numbers

Lowest

0 1 2 3 4 5 6 7 8 9

Dear Helper

This game will help your child to practise ordering numbers to 100. Begin by cutting out the number cards at the side of the page. Turn them face down on the table then take turns to pick up two cards to make a two-digit number. Write each two-digit number in the box until you have a total of 20 numbers. Now write the numbers in order on the path, starting with the lowest at the bottom. If your child has difficulties with numbers to 100, just make numbers to 30. If they find this too easy, use three cards each time to make three-digit numbers.

Inversions

3 + 2 = 5	5 − 2 = 3
5 + 10 = 15	15 − 10 = 5
14 + 5 = 19	19 − 5 = 14
11 + 10 = 21	21 − 10 = 11
13 + 12 = 25	25 − 12 = 13
15 + 20 = 35	35 − 20 = 15
16 + 30 = 46	46 − 30 = 16
20 + 23 = 43	43 − 23 = 20
24 + 35 = 59	59 − 35 = 24
26 + 32 = 58	58 − 32 = 26

Dear Helper

This activity will help to reinforce the work that your child has been doing on inversions. They have been learning that addition is the opposite of subtraction and that they can work out the answers to subtraction calculations from knowing the matching additions. Help your child to cut out the cards then jumble them up to play a matching game. See how long it takes your child to match the addition with the subtraction.

Name _____   Date _____

Split the number

- Choose two numbers to add together using the partitioning method.
- Remember to keep your biggest number whole and partition the smaller number into tens and units.

15	23				

For example:

Numbers chosen: 15 and 23	Partitioning: 23 + 10 + 5 = 33 + 5	My answer is: 38
Numbers chosen:	Partitioning:	My answer is:
Numbers chosen:	Partitioning:	My answer is:
Numbers chosen:	Partitioning:	My answer is:
Numbers chosen:	Partitioning:	My answer is:

- Now make up some more on the back of this sheet.

Dear Helper
Your child has been learning how to add two numbers by keeping the biggest number whole and partitioning the other number in to tens and units before adding them together. For example, 23 + 12 = 23 + 10 + 2 = 33 + 2 = 35. An example has been done above. The numbers have been specially chosen for your child's ability level. Ask them to explain the strategy to you before beginning the activity.

Name	Date

 # Which method?

◼ Choose from these strategies to work out the calculations.

Near doubles		Rounding and adjusting
Counting on	Partitioning the last number	Number bonds

Calculation

Strategy

Answer

Calculation

Strategy

Answer

Calculation

Strategy

Answer

Calculation

Strategy

Answer

Calculation

Strategy

Answer

Calculation

Strategy

Answer

Calculation

Strategy

Answer

Calculation

Strategy

Answer

Dear Helper
Your child has been learning to add and subtract using different strategies and for the activity above, they will need to choose the best strategy to solve different calculations. Please let your child explain their choice of strategy to you. The calculations have been specially chosen to match your child's knowledge and understanding of these strategies.

Pence to pounds

◾ Look at the numbers below. For each example, convert the number of pence into pounds and pence.

125p ➡ £1.25   302p ➡ £3.02

175p ➡   345p ➡

225p ➡   269p ➡

180p ➡   199p ➡

◾ Now add these amounts together and write the answers in pounds and pence.

50p + 80p	60p + 90p	70p + 80p
50p + 70p	75p + 80p	75p + 75p

PHOTOCOPIABLE

www.scholastic.co.uk

Name _____ Date _____

 # What a problem!

◢ Solve the problems below. Show how you worked them out.

Four oranges cost ☐ each. How much change would you get from ☐ ? Show your working out.	Three apples cost ☐ each. How much change would you get from ☐ ? Show your working out.
Five pears cost ☐ each. How much change would you get from ☐ ? Show your working out.	Three apples cost ☐ each. How much change would you get from ☐ ? Show your working out.
Ten bananas cost ☐ each. How much change would you get from ☐ ? Show your working out.	Two biscuits cost ☐ each. How much change would you get from ☐ ? Show your working out.

◢ Make up some problems on the back of the sheet for your Helper to answer.

Dear Helper
This activity will provide your child with practise in solving word problems. Your child's teacher will have chosen numbers in each example to match your child's ability.

Measure it

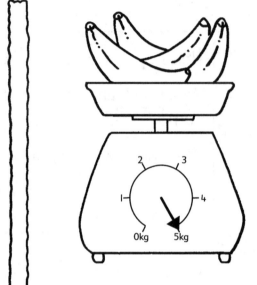

The bananas weigh

_____ kg.

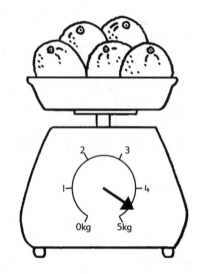

The oranges weigh just

over _____ kg.

The ribbon

is _____

cm long.

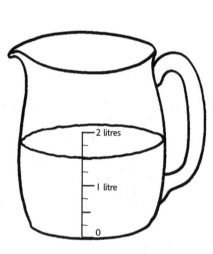

There is _____ litres of

liquid in the jug.

There is _____ litres of

liquid in the jug.

Dear Helper

This activity will reinforce the work on measures that your child has been doing in class. Encourage your child to read the measurements for each picture and to write the answers in the boxes. The first one has been done for you.

Name

Date

Draw the measures

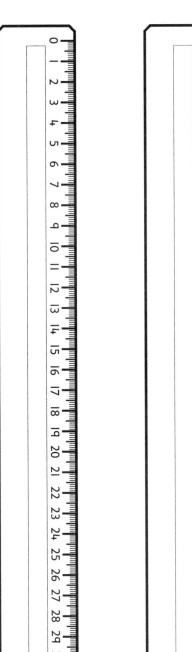

Draw an arrow to show half a litre.

Draw an arrow to show
quarter of a litre.

Draw an
arrow to
show 15cm.

Draw an arrow to show
a measurement between
15cm and 20cm.

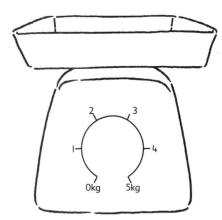

Draw an arrow to show 4.5kg.

Dear Helper
This activity will help to reinforce the work that your child has been doing on measures. Encourage
your child to look at each picture in turn and read the instructions, then help them to draw an arrow
on each picture in the appropriate place.

Name   Date

Position, direction or movement?

◼ Draw lines to match the vocabulary to its correct box depending on whether they are a postion, direction or movement.

Position words

clockwise

under

anti-clockwise

slide

corner

outside

right

quarter turn

towards

Direction words

right angle

straight line

backwards

higher

lower

across

front

back

beside

sideways

Movement words

middle

left

roll

Dear Helper
Encourage your child to look at the words above. Challenge them to match the vocabulary associated with position, direction or movement, to the correct boxes. If your child would like a challenge, ask them to make up a story using some of these words. If your child has difficulty, try to work out the specific words they need to practise and then practise these with them.

PHOTOCOPIABLE

www.scholastic.co.uk

Name	Date

Give us a clue!

◢ Match each statement to the correct shape below.

I have four sides that are equal lengths.	I have three sides and three corners.
Shape:	Shape:

I have two faces shaped like circles.	I have one face shaped like a circle.
Shape:	Shape:

There is nothing straight about me at all.	I have at least two square faces.
Shape:	Shape:

I have a round face and straight sides.	I have six faces.
Shape:	Shape:

circle   square   triangle   sphere

cylinder   cone   cube   cuboid

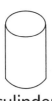

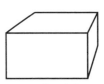

Dear Helper
Your child has been learning about the properties of shapes. Read the clues out and ask your child to tell you the name of the shape and write the answer in the appropriate place. If your child has difficulty, ask them to point to the picture and write the name in for them. For a challenge, ask them to make up another clue for each shape.

PHOTOCOPIABLE

www.scholastic.co.uk

ALL NEW 100 MATHS HOMEWORK AND ASSESSMENT · YEAR 2

Snaky stripes

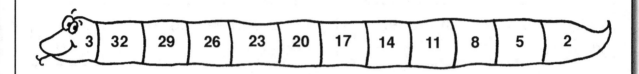

| 3 | 32 | 29 | 26 | 23 | 20 | 17 | 14 | 11 | 8 | 5 | 2 |

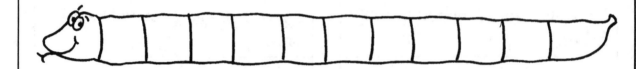

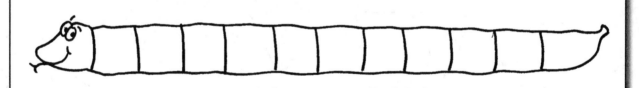

Dear Helper

Your child has been learning to count on and back in steps of three, four and five. In this activity, please focus on counting back. Your child's teacher has filled in a starting number and step number on each snake. Encourage your child to complete each snake by counting back in steps of that number. The first example has been done for you.

Name _____ Date _____

How many ways?

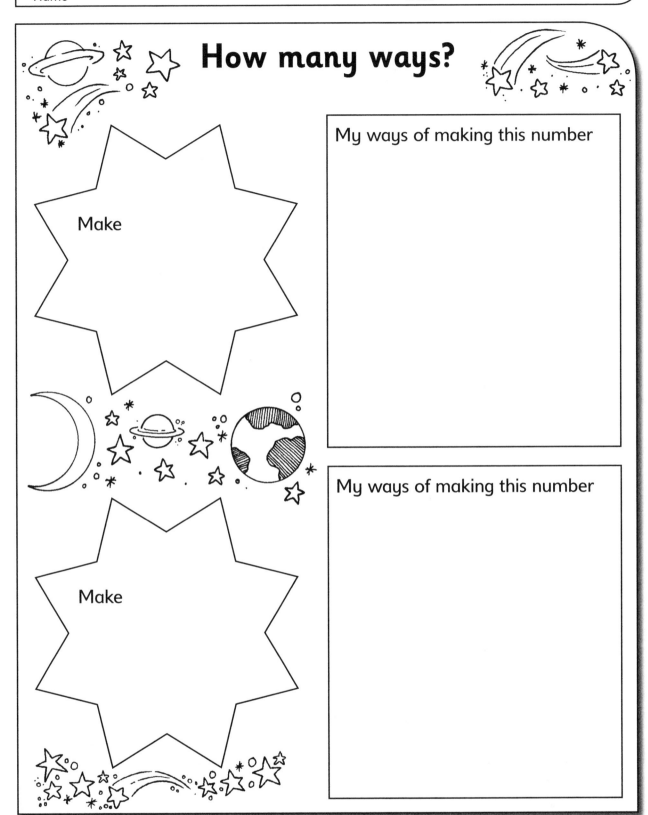

Make

My ways of making this number

Make

My ways of making this number

Dear Helper

Your child has been investigating ways of making numbers. The numbers in the stars have been chosen specially for your child. Encourage them to find at least 15 different ways to make each number. For example, if the number was 24, they could use some of the following ways: half of 48; 25 − 1; 20 + 4; 10 x 2 + 4; 12 x 2 and so on. If your child is having difficulty, lower the target to ten. If your child needs a challenge, ask them to think of interesting and complex ways of reaching the totals.

Bridging ten

Dear Helper

This game will provide practise in adding numbers and adjusting by one. You will need two dice and a different coloured counter each. Place your counters on 'Start'. The first player should roll both dice and make the smallest two-digit number they can. Using the first number in the game (nine), they should add nine to their number by adding ten and taking away one. They should then move their counter according to the number of tens in their answer. For example, if you throw a three and a six, you would make 36. Add nine (36 + 10 − 1) to give 45. There are four tens in 45, so move on four spaces to land on 11. On the next go, you would add 11 to your two-digit number (add ten and then one). If your child has difficulty, use one dice, adding nine or 11. For a challenge, ask them to look at the two posible numbers they could make and decide which wil allow them to make the most moves.

PHOTOCOPIABLE

Doubles and halves

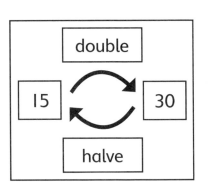

◼ Double or halve the numbers below to fill in the missing boxes.

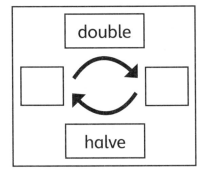

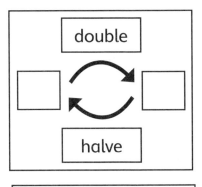

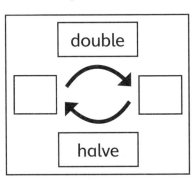

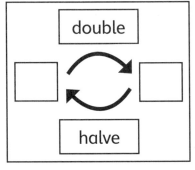

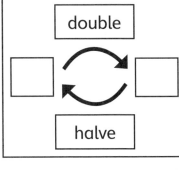

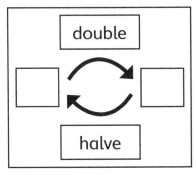

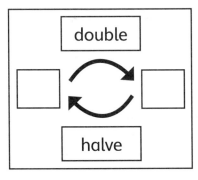

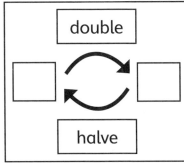

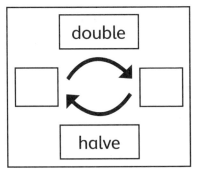

Dear Helper
This activity will provide practise in doubling and halving numbers. Remind your child that doubling is making something twice as big, and halving is making it half as big. Your child's teacher will have chosen numbers appropriate to your child's ability. An example has been done for you.

PHOTOCOPIABLE

www.scholastic.co.uk

ALL NEW 100 MATHS HOMEWORK AND ASSESSMENT · YEAR 2

Name _____ Date _____

Which coins?

 1p

 2p

 5p

10p

 20p

 50p

 £1

 £2

◼ Look at the coins above. Using the least amount of coins, make the total amount of money shown in the boxes below.

£1.25
£1 + 20p + 5 = £1.25

Coins © Crown Copyright, The Royal Mint

Dear Helper
Your child has been learning how to make different total amounts using different coins. Encourage them to use the least number of coins to make each total amount (they can use two or more of the same coin if necessary), and to write a number sentence to describe which coins they used. Your child's teacher has chosen appropriate amounts of money for your child to make. Please check that your child has correctly positioned the point between pounds and pence. An example has been done for you.

PHOTOCOPIABLE

Name	Date

 # Equivalents

◢ Match the shaded pictures to their corresponding fraction.

 $\dfrac{2}{2}$

 $\dfrac{1}{2}$

 $\dfrac{1}{4}$

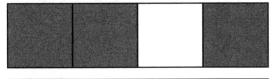 $\dfrac{2}{4}$

 $\dfrac{4}{4}$

 1

 $\dfrac{3}{4}$

Number sentences:

$\dfrac{1}{2} = \boxed{} + \boxed{}$

1 whole $= \boxed{} + \boxed{}$

$\dfrac{3}{4} = \boxed{} + \boxed{}$

Dear Helper

This activity will help your child to practise their fraction work. Encourage them to look at the pictures and work out the fraction that is shaded, then to match the fraction to the equivalent label. Afterwards, encourage your child to fill in the number sentences at the bottom of the page.

www.scholastic.co.uk

Name _____   Date _____

Fraction problems

Emma saw ☐ lions at the zoo. A quarter of them were very hungry but the rest were not. How many lions were very hungry?

My answer and how I worked it out

Ravi went to feed the penguins. He was given ☐ fish. He threw half of them in the water and half on to the rocks. How many fish were in the water?

My answer and how I worked it out

Tom saw ☐ monkeys. A quarter of them were swinging in the trees and the rest were sleeping. How many monkeys were sleeping?

My answer and how I worked it out

Jade saw ☐ parrots. Half of them were squawking. How many were not squawking?

My answer and how I worked it out

Oliver saw ☐ turtles. A quarter of them were adult turtles and the rest were baby turtles. How many of them were baby turtles?

My answer and how I worked it out

Dear Helper
This activity will help your child to practise the problem solving work that they have been doing in class. Help your child to read and answer each problem. The numbers have been specially chosen for your child.

Can you find my partner?

Yesterday	The day before today	60 minutes
Hour	Week	Seven days
Month	Between four and five weeks	Fortnight
Two weeks	Monday to Friday	Weekdays
Wednesday	The day before Thursday	Morning
Before midday	Tomorrow	The day after today
Yesterday	The day before today	Friday
The day after Thursday	April	The month before May
November	The month after October	60 seconds
1 minute	Saturday and Sunday	The weekend

Dear Helper

This game will reinforce your child's understanding of measurements of time. Cut out the word cards and place them face down. The first player should turn over two cards. If the cards show the same amount of time, for example 'Week' and '7 days', the player keeps them. If they do not match, the player should turn them over again and let the next player take a turn. The winner is the player with the most pairs. If your child has difficulty, play with the cards facing up. For a challenge, ask them to make up a sentence using one of the words they have matched before keeping it.

PHOTOCOPIABLE

Match the time

	7:00		2:30
	1:15		3:45
	10:00		6:30
	7:15		4:45
	3:00		11:30

Dear Helper

This activity will help your child to read the time on both analogue and digital clocks. Cut out the cards and place them face down. The first player should turn over two cards. If the cards show the same time in analogue and digital format, then the player keeps those cards. If they do not show the same time, the player should turn them over again and let the next player take a turn. The winner is the player with the most pairs. If your child has difficulty, play the game with the cards face up. For a challenge, ask them to make a sentence using one of the words they have matched before keeping it.

PHOTOCOPIABLE

Name   Date

  # Faulty graph

◾ Find the seven faults with the graph. Correct the graph and then write down as many facts as you can using the information provided.

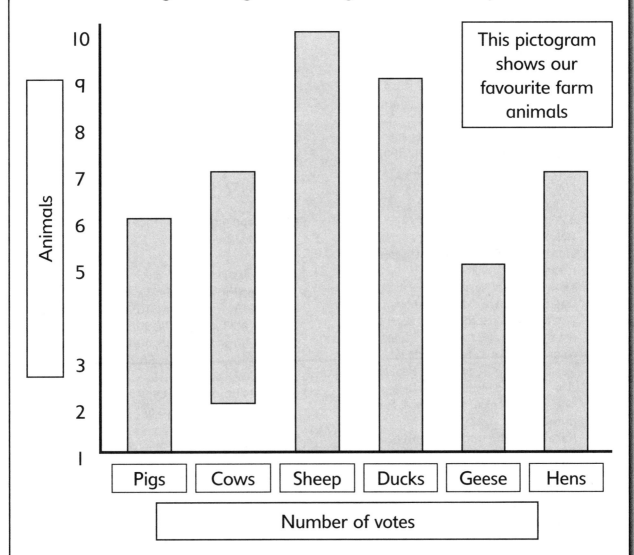

The votes for our favourite farm animals were

Pigs 6   Cows 7   Sheep 10   Ducks 9   Geese 5   Hens 5

Dear Helper

This activity will provide practise in organising data. There are seven mistakes on this graph for your child to find and correct. Help your child to find them all and to draw or write on the correct answers. When they have found the faults, encourage them to write down as many facts as they can find from the graph, for example, the favourite and least favourite animals. If your child has difficulty, ask them to point at things that look wrong in the graph. For a challenge, ask them to draw a correct graph.

PHOTOCOPIABLE

www.scholastic.co.uk   ALL NEW 100 MATHS HOMEWORK AND ASSESSMENT · YEAR 2

Answer sheet

Autumn Term

P13 **Number line** Answers will vary.

P14 **Combining cards** 16 possible answers: 11; 12; 15; 17; 31; 32; 35; 37; 41; 42; 45; 47; 71; 72; 75; 77.

P15 **Arrow sentences** Depends on numbers filled in by teacher.

P16 **The name game** 25 possible answers: 23; 24; 27; 28; 32; 34; 37; 38; 42; 43; 47; 48; 72; 73; 74; 78; 82; 83; 84; 87 (written as figures and words)

P17 **Get some help!** Answers will vary.

P18 **Toy shopping** 11p = 10p + 1p; 30p = 20p + 10p; 21p = 20p + 1p; 32p = 20p + 10p + 2p; 26p = 20p + 5p + 1p; 28p = 20p + 5p + 2p + 1p; 33p = 20p + 10p + 2p + 1p; 42p = 20p + 20p + 2p

P19 **How much?** Answers will vary.

P20 **Word search** Check that the children have found all of the words.

P21 **Time for snap!** No answers.

P22 **Describe me** 1. 6 sides, 6 corners, symmetrical, Hexagon; 2. 8 sides, 8 corners, not symmetrical, Octagon; 3. 5 sides, 5 corners, not symmetrical, Pentagon; 4. 5 sides, 5 corners, symmetrical, Pentagon; 5. 8 sides, 8 corners, symmetrical, Octagon; 6. 6 sides, 6 corners, not symmetrical, Hexagon.

P23 **In the bin** No answers.

P24 **Race along the track** No answers.

P25 **Up the ladder!** Answers will vary.

P26 **Beat the clock!** 1; 2; 5; 3; 3; 5; 2; 0; 1; 7; 4; 8; 2; 3; 4; 1; 2; 3; 4; 0; 9; 8; 10; 9.

P27 **Loopy lines** Answers will vary.

P28 **Double trouble maze**

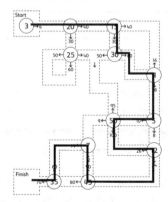

P29 **Quarter mastery**
The cross, hexagon and double-headed arrow can be quartered. The pentagon,

P30 **Percy's hungry** No answers.

P31 **Reading scales** 10cm; 3.5kg; ½ litre; 1 litre.

P32 **Telling the time**

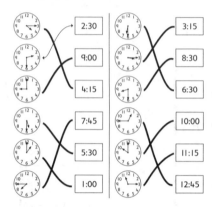

P33 **Shape puzzles** Depends on values chosen by teacher.

Spring Term

P38 **Spotting multiples** Twos: 2, 4, 6, 8, 10, 12, 14, 16, 18, 20; Fives: 10,15, 20, 25; Tens: 10, 20; Twos: 32, 34, 36, 38, 40, 42, 44, 46, 48, 50 and Fives: 35, 40, 45, 50; Fives: 50, 55, 60 and Tens: 50, 60; Multiples of two: 44, 12, 78, 14, 16, 38.

P39 **Dots before your eyes** 3 groups of 10 and 3 left = 33; 4 groups of 5 and 4 left = 24; 8 groups of 2 = 16

P40 **Spider charts** Answers will vary.

P41 **Rounding up** Answers will vary.

P42 **Totals to ten** Answers will vary.

P43 **Partitioning and recombining** Answers will vary.

P44 **Making problems** Answers will vary.

P45 **All the same value** Multiples of 10p up to 60p; Multiples of 5p up to 30p.

P46 **Measures** String: 12cm; Apples: exactly 2kg; Bananas: just over 4kg; Liquid: just over 2 litres; Liquid: just under 1 litre.

P47 **Where is the arrow?** Higher; clockwise; anti-clockwise; lower; behind; in front; beside; quarter turn; right angle.

P48 **Stepping stones** Depends on numbers chosen by teacher.

P49 **Right or wrong?** 1. right; 2. right; 3. wrong (more than three possible ways).

heart and triangle cannot be quartered.

Answer sheet

P50 **Fill your ladder** No answers.
P51 **Grouping** Depends on numbers chosen by teacher.
P52 **Investigate these facts** Depends on numbers chosen by teacher.
P53 **Halves and quarters** Answers will vary.
P54 **Time crossword**
Across: 2 morning; 4 after; 5 afternoon; 7 early; 9 late; 10 evenings; 11 digital. **Down:** 1 fortnight; 3 watch; 4 analogue; 5 seconds; 8 minute.
P55 **Favourite colours** Answers will vary.
P56 **Sorting it out** Yellow, white and red are the favourite colours.

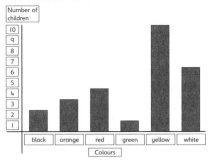

Summer Term
P61 **Odds and evens** Answers will vary.
P62 **The ordering game** Answers will vary.
P63 **Inversions** 3 + 2 = 5 / 5 - 2 = 3; 5 +10 = 15 / 15 - 10 = 5; 14 + 5 = 19 / 19 - 5 = 14; 11 + 10 = 21 / 21 - 10 = 11; 13 + 12 = 25/ 25 - 12 = 13; 15 + 20 = 35 / 35 - 20 = 15; 16 + 30 = 46 / 46 - 30 = 16; 20 + 23 = 43 / 43 - 23 = 20; 24 + 35 = 59 / 59 - 35 = 24; 26 + 32 = 58 / 58 - 32 = 26.
P64 **Split the number** Depends on numbers chosen by teacher.
P65 **Which method** Depends on calculations chosen by teacher.
P66 **Pence to pounds** 175p = £1.75; 345p = £3.45; 225p = £2.25; 269p = £2.69; 180p = £1.80; 199p = £1.99; 130p/£1.30; 150p/£1.50; 150p/£1.50; 120p/£1.20; 155p/£1.55; 150p/£1.50.
P67 **What a problem!** Depends on numbers chosen by teacher.
P68 **Measure it** Ribbon: 23cm; Bananas: 5kg; Oranges: just over 4.5kg; Liquid: 1.5 litres; Liquid: 2 litres.
P69 **Draw the measures** Check arrows are accurately drawn.

P70 **Position, direction or movement?**
Position: under; higher; lower; corner; outside; right; back; beside; front; middle; left. **Direction:** clockwise; anti-clockwise; towards; backwards; sideways; across. **Movement:** roll; slide; right angle; straight line; quarter turn.
P71 **Give us a clue!** Square; triangle; cylinder; circle or cone; sphere; cube or cuboid.
P72 **Snaky stripes** Depends on numbers chosen by teacher.
P73 **How many ways?** Depends on numbers chosen by teacher.
P74 **Bridging ten** No answers.
P75 **Doubles and halves** Depends on numbers chosen by teacher.
P76 **Which coins?** Depends on totals chosen by teacher.
P77 **Equivalents!**

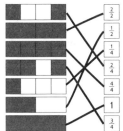

1 whole = ½ + ½; ½ = ¼ + ¼; ¾ = ½ + ¼.
P78 **Fraction problems** Depends on numbers chosen by teacher.
P79 **Can you find my partner?** Yesterday/The day before today; 60 minutes/Hour; Week/Seven days; Month/Between four and five weeks; Fortnight/Two weeks; Monday to Friday/Weekdays; Wednesday/The day before Thursday; Morning/Before midday; Tomorrow/ The day after today; Yesterday/ The day before today; Friday/The day after Thursday; April/The month before May; November/The month after October; 60 seconds/1 minute; Saturday and Sunday/ The weekend.
P80 **Match the time** Check individuals' understanding.
P81 **Faulty graph** No zero on vertical axis; no four on vertical axis; each axis label is wrong - they need switching over (x 2 faults); Cow column not sitting on horizontal axis; wrong title - block graph not pictogram; wrong number of hens shown on graph.

Year 2 Key objectives

a Describe and extend simple number sequences: count on or back in ones or tens, starting from any two-digit number.

b Recognise odd and even numbers.

c Read, write and order whole numbers to at least 100.

d Know what each digit in a two-digit number represents, including zero as a place holder.

e Understand that subtraction is the inverse of addition.

f Know by heart all addition and subtraction facts for each number to at least 10.

g Use knowledge that addition can be done in any order to do mental calculations more efficiently.

h State the subtraction corresponding to a given addition and vice versa.

i Understand the operation of multiplication as repeated addition or as describing an array.

j Know and use halving as the inverse of doubling.

k Know by heart multiplication factsf or the 2- and 10- times tables.

l Choose and use appropriate operations and efficient calculation strategies to solve problems, explaining how a problem was solved.

m Estimate, measure and compare lengths, masses and capacities, using standard units; suggest suitable units and equipment for such measurements.

n Read a simple scale to the nearest labelled division, including using a ruler to draw and measure lines to the nearest centimetre.

o Use the mathematical names for common 3D and 2D shapes. Sort and describe some of their features.

p Use mathematical vocabulary to describe position, direction and movement.

Introduction

The planning for the assessment units is based upon the NNS medium-term plans. There is an assessment unit for each end of half term, as well as end-of-year assessments. Each unit consists of two detailed lesson plans, each assessing one of the Key objectives, with an accompanying photocopiable activity sheet for each lesson. The notes include suggestions for further work where children have not met the objective. There are additional oral and mental, practical and written activities covering the range of Key objectives taught that half-term, with photocopiable assessment sheets for written work. For the end-of-year assessment there is an assessment covering all the Year 2 Key objectives, a mental assessment and a written assessment. The end-of-year assessments mirror the style of the national tests or QCA non-statutory tests. Letters alongside each objective (see left) appear alongside each assessment activity to help you identify which objectives are covered by each activity.

Using the assessment units

Choose the half-term assessment that matches your planning needs. From your ongoing teacher assessments, identify the children that you believe have achieved specific Key objectives. Now decide upon the children who you suspect may have met the Key objective/s but for whom you have no firm assessment data (a class record sheet has been provided for this purpose). These children can form the target group for assessment; arrange for them to work with an adult during practical activities, who should use the probing questions included in the assessment notes for teachers. Ask all the children to complete the written assessments, putting the probing questions to the targeted group.

Supporting teaching assistants

Provide the teaching assistant with details of the activity (whether practical or written). Discuss the probing questions to be used and how responses will be recorded – did the child give appropriate, correct responses to the questions? Was a specific question answered inappropriately? Where the latter occurs, some additional notes about what the child failed to understand would be helpful for planning future teaching. Discuss the outcomes of the assessment activity together and make notes about individual children.

Assessment for learning

Assessment is always for a purpose – here it is to check what individual children understand, know and can do, and where they need further teaching in order to achieve the Key objectives. Use the outcomes of the assessment for forward planning for teaching and for homework provision. The *All New 100 Maths Lessons* (Scholastic) series provides detailed planning grids for each term, which can be used to identify further activities to support those who need more experiences in particular topics.

Assess and Review

Key objectives to be assessed

Assessment Lesson 1: **Use knowledge that addition can be done in any order to do mental calculations more efficiently; Choose and use appropriate operations and efficient calculation strategies to solve problems, explaining how each problem was solved.**

Assessment Lesson 2: **Use the mathematical names for common 2D and 3D shapes; sort   shapes and describe some of their features**

Photocopiable pages

'How? (p87); Guess the shape! (p89); Numeral cards (p90); Assessment test (pages 91-92)

Equipment

Whiteboards and pens; length of string about 2m long; ruler; metre stick; plastic bag

containing between 1kg and 2kg of sand; weighing scales; container with between 1 litre and 2 litres of coloured water; measuring jug; large cube and compare bear; shapes: cuboid, pyramid, sphere, cone, cylinder.

Assessment Activities

Mental maths assessment

1. Read, write and order whole numbers to at least 100 [c]

Ask the children to write 8 on their whiteboards and then follow instructions, for example: *add 1, add 40, take away 5, what number do you have? Add 100, take away 50, what do you have?*

Probing questions

● *Which number says 34? How do you know?*
● *How are these numbers the same/different?*

2. Know what each digit in a two-digit number represents, including zero [d]

Ask the children to make as many two and/or three-digit numbers from two/three separate digit cards. Ask what each number actually is, for example, the 2 in 206. Ask the children to order the numbers from smallest to biggest.

Probing questions

● *Tell me a number that comes between these two numbers.*
● *Why is the zero there?*

Practical maths assessment

1. Estimate, measure then compare lengths, masses and capacities using standard units; [m]

2. Read a simple scale to the nearest labelled division [n]

Using measuring equipment, work through the following activities:

● Show a 15cm line on a piece of paper. Ask the children to estimate its length, say what equipment and units they could use to measure it and why. Finally ask them to measure it accurately.
● Repeat with a plastic bag filled with 1kg of sand.
● Repeat with a container that will hold 2 litres of coloured water.
● Ask the children to draw lines of 5cms, 10cms and 20cms on a piece of paper.

Probing questions

● *Can you show me something that you think is: a) longer/shorter; b) lighter/heavier; c) less/more?*

Written maths assessment

Distribute the Assessment test on p91-92.

1. Choose and use appropriate operations and efficient calculation strategies to solve problems [l]

Probing questions

● *How did you solve this?*
● *Was there another method you could have used?*

2. Use mathematical vocabulary to describe position, direction and movement [p]

Probing questions

● *If this was in the opposite position, where would it be?*
● *Can you describe where this bear is in relation to the cube? Where is it now?*

WEEK 7 LESSON 1 ▢ Half-term assessment

Add them up

Key objectives:
Use knowledge that addition can be done in any order to do mental calculations more efficiently; choose and use appropriate operations and efficient calculation strategies to solve problems, explaining how each problem was solved.

What you need
● A copy of 'Add them up!' assessment sheet for each child.

Further support
Work with less confident children, listening to their strategies and writing down what they say. Note whether they have alternative methods or if they either partition or use their fingers.

Oral and mental starter

Write the following sets of numbers on the board:

2	14	8	
3	9	27	
10	3	10	7

For each row ask the children to tell a partner how they would total the numbers quickly. Encourage strategies like finding numbers that total ten and doubling (see examples below). Review the totals and the strategies used. Example strategies include:

$(2 + 8) = 10; 10 + 14 = 24$
$(27 + 3) = 30; 30 + 9 = 39$
$(10 \times 2) = 20; (3 + 7) = 10; 20 + 10 = 30$

Main assessment activity

Ask the children to think about the different strategies they have learned for addition and discuss these with a neighbour and then with the class. Discuss partitioning, doubling, near doubling, looking for numbers that total ten or a multiple of ten and adding nine by adding ten and adjusting.

Ask the children to consider which strategies to use for the following calculation: $12 + 13 + 9 + 8$. There are several. Ask them to discuss with a neighbour which one they prefer and then tell the rest of the class. Talk about the inefficiency of just using fingers in terms of time and accuracy.

Give the children the 'Add them up!' assessment sheet to complete on their own. Model what you expect the children to do with the following sum: $6 + 9 + 12 + 4$. For example:
● *I added 6 and 4 to get 10. I added 9 and 12 to get 21, by adding 10 to the 12 and taking away 1.*
● *I then added 10 and 20 and 2 to get 32.*
● *I can show my workings by writing: $(6 + 4) + (10 + 12 - 1) = 10 + 21 = 31$*
● *Is there another way?*

During the assessment activity, ask groups probing questions such as:
● *How did you add those numbers? Can you tell me another way of adding them? Would this way give the same answer? Why?*
● *What do you look for when you decide the best order for adding numbers?*
● *Which numbers are near doubles?*

Plenary

By the end of the lesson the children should be able to confidently use a variety of strategies for adding mentally and be able to decide on the best ones to use in different situations. Invite them to share some of the strategies that they used to answer their calculations. For each, ask the rest of the class: *Did any one use a different strategy? Which do you think is the best? Why?*

WEEK 7 LESSON 1 🔲 **Half-term assessment**

| Name | Date |

Add them up!

🔲 Work out the answers to these addition questions.
🔲 Write down the methods you used in the boxes.

6 + 10 + 6 = This is how I worked it out	15 + 7 + 3 + 15 = This is how I worked it out
12 + 13 = This is how I worked it out	8 + 9 + 4 = This is how I worked it out
15 + 13 + 5 = This is how I worked it out	25 + 30 + 25 = This is how I worked it out
19 + 7 + 3 = This is how I worked it out	14 + 16 = This is how I worked it out
13 + 13 + 14 = This is how I worked it out	2 + 18 + 8 + 12 = This is how I worked it out

PHOTOCOPIABLE

What shape am I?

<table>
<tr><td>

Key objective:
Use the mathematical names for common 2D and 3D shapes; sort shapes and describe some of their features.

</td></tr>
</table>

What you need
● Selection of regular and irregular 2D shapes: circle, triangle, square, rectangle, pentagon, hexagon, octagon; selection of 3D shapes: sphere, cube, cuboid, cylinder, cone, pyramid for each child; box; a copy of activity sheet 'What shape am I?' for each child.

Further support
Organise less confident children into a group so that they can work together. Ask an adult to read the instructions and observe and record each child's observations about the shapes.

Oral and mental starter

Hide one of the 2D or 3D shapes in a box. Slowly reveal it asking the children to put up their hands when they think they know what it might be.
Ask: *What shape could this be? Could it be another shape? What shape can it not be? How do you know? What is special about this shape?* Repeat several times with different shapes.

Main assessment activity

Remind the children that they did some work on shapes earlier in the term. Ask them to tell you all of the 2D and 3D shape names that they can remember. Write the names on the board. Ask them to describe each shape in turn, including the number and type of faces, sides, edges, symmetry and corners. Have a box of shapes in front of you and invite individual children to find the correct ones as they are described.
Ask: *How do you know this shape is not a cuboid? How do you know that it is 3D shape?*

Copy the assessment sheet on to an OHT. Look at the picture of the cube, then ask the children to tell you its name and to write it in the appropriate place on the sheet. Ask them to show you, using their fingers, how many faces the cube has, then count them and add that to the sheet. Do the same for the sides and corners. Finally, look at the shape of each face. *Can the children recognise that they are squares?* Add this to the sheet. Once they understand the instructions, give each child the assessment sheet to complete independently.

Plenary

Think of a shape and ask the children to ask you questions about its properties to which you can only answer *Yes* or *No*. They are allowed no more than ten questions after which they should be able to tell what your shape is. Hold up two 2D shapes, such as a square and a triangle. Ask: *What is the same about these shapes? What is different?* Do the same with two 3D shapes. By the end of the lesson the children should be able demonstrate that they know the properties of the required 2D and 3D shapes and should understand the terms *faces, edges, sides* and *corners*.

| Name | | Date | |

What shape am I?

- Look carefully at each shape.
- Write the name of the shape, and its properties, in the box alongside each one.
- Choose from these strategies to work out the calculations.

Name _____

Number of sides _____

Number of corners _____

How many ways
is it symmetrical? _____

Name _____

Number of faces _____

Number of sides _____

Number of corners _____

Shape of the faces _____

Name _____

Number of sides _____

Number of corners _____

How many ways
is it symmetrical? _____

Name _____

Number of faces _____

Number of sides _____

Number of corners _____

Shape of the faces _____

Name _____

Number of faces _____

Number of sides _____

Number of corners _____

Shape of the faces _____

Name _____

Number of sides _____

Number of corners _____

How many ways
is it symmetrical? _____

Name _____

Number of sides _____

Number of corners _____

How many ways
is it symmetrical? _____

Name _____

Number of faces _____

Number of sides _____

Number of corners _____

Shape of the faces _____

www.scholastic.co.uk

ALL NEW 100 MATHS HOMEWORK AND ASSESSMENT · YEAR 2

Numeral cards

Use these cards for different number activities and games.

0	1	2
3	4	5
6	7	8
9	10	

Name   Date

Assessment 1

- Here are some problems for you to work out.
- Write your answer in the small box. Show how you worked the problems out.

1. Paul has 6 marbles, Ben has 8 and Sue has 12.
How many do they have altogether?

Show how you worked this out

2. Anna has 63p. She wants to buy a card.
The card costs 9p more than she has.
How much is the card?

Show how you worked this out

3. Ben collects toy soldiers.
He has 16 captains and 8 generals.
How many does he have altogether?

Show how you worked this out

Name   Date

Assessment 2

1. Write the correct word to match the position of the arrow.

Words to choose from:
left   right   behind   in front   beside

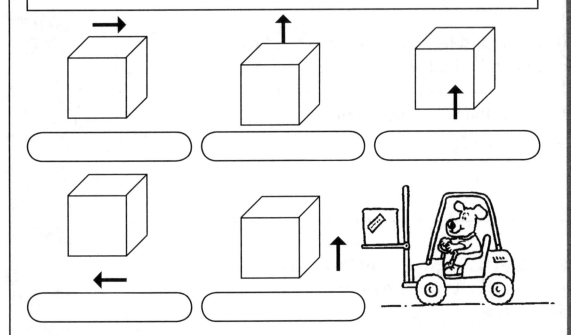

2. Write the correct word to match the direction or turn of the arrow.

Words to choose from:
quarter turn   right   clockwise   left   anti-clockwise

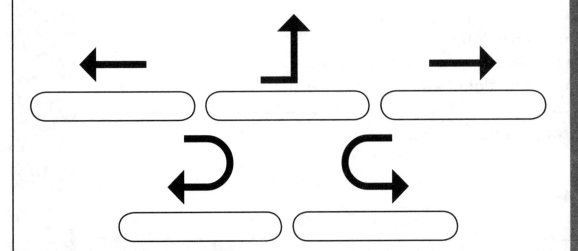

Assess and Review

Key objectives to be assessed
Assessment lesson 1: **Describe and extend simple number sequences (odd/even numbers, counting on or back in ones or tens from any two-digit number).**
Assessment lesson 2: **Read a simple scale to the nearest labelled division, including using a ruler to draw and measure lines to the nearest centimetre.**

Photocopiable pages
'Number snake (page 95); Measuring up (page 97); Spider charts (page 98); Assessment test (p99-100).

Equipment
Individual whiteboards and pens; counters.

Assessment Activities

Mental maths assessment

1. Read and write whole numbers to at least 100 c
Ask the children to write numbers on their whiteboards, for example: 15, 51, 135, 153
Probing questions
● *Look at the numbers, which says 51, which says 15? How do you know?*
● *How are these numbers the same? How are they different?*

2. Order whole numbers to at least 100 c
Give each child five number cards. Ask them to order the cards from smallest to largest.
Probing questions
● *What clues did you look for to help you put the cards in the correct order?*
● *Tell me a number that comes in between these two numbers.*

3. Know by heart all addition facts for each number to at least 10 f
Draw this on the board (square) + (circle) = 9. Repeat for 6, 7 and 8.
Probing questions
● *Look at this number sentence. What could the two missing numbers be? What else could they be?*
● *Can you show me all the pairs that make nine?*

4. Know by heart multiplication facts for the 2- and 10-times tables k
Using the two- and ten-times table multiplication spider charts on p98, point to a number and encourage the child to write the answer on a

sheet of paper. Draw this on the board: (square) × (circle) = 20.
Probing questions
● *What could the missing numbers be?*
● *Where could you put them? Does the order matter?*

Written maths assessment
Give out copies of p90 and p100.

1. Count on or back in ones or tens from any two-digit number a
● *If you count in tens from 20 to 100, how many tens will you count?*
● *If I started counting from 12 and counted on another 12, what number will I get to?*

2. Choose and use appropriate operations and efficient calculation strategies to solve problems l
● *Which of these can you easily work out in your head? How would you do that?*
● *Which might you need to use jottings for? Why?*

3. Understand the operation of multiplication as repeated addition or subtraction or as describing an array i
● *How many dots are there? Explain how you can work it out without counting.*
● *What number sentence can you write to record your method using the × symbol and now the +?*

4. Recognise odd and even numbers b
● *What is special about an even number?*
● *What numbers do all odd numbers end with?*

Number snake

Oral and mental starter

Using a counting stick, rehearse counting on and back in twos, threes, fours and fives initially from zero. As you use the stick, ensure that you move your finger backwards and forwards, making jumps of different sizes.

Ask: *What number will be next? Which number comes before this one? What will be here? Why? Is this an odd number? How do you know?*

Main assessment activity

Give each pair of children a copy of the 'Number snake' sheet, a spinner and a counter each. Model the game with a volunteer. Put two counters on zero. The first player spins the spinner and counts in steps of that number. For example, if player one spins a 2, they should count on from zero, place the counter on the number 2 and write down the next three numbers in the sequence: 4, 6, 8 (with their counter remaining on 2). On their next turn, the child should begin counting from 2. For example, if 10 is spun, they move their counter to 12 and write down the next three numbers in the sequence (this time counting in tens, so: 22, 32, 42). Players can check the correct number sequences using the board or a counting stick. Players take it in turns to play, counting on from the number on which they land. The game ends when one of the players reaches the end of the game board.

Sit with pairs to observe and ask probing questions: *If you count in tens from 23, which digit changes? Why does the units digit stay the same? If you start at 85 and count back in tens, what would be the smallest number you would reach? Would 12 be one of the numbers you say? Why not? Point to the number 35 What is this type of number called? Can you tell me something special about odd numbers? What about even numbers?*

Plenary

Write these numbers on the board: 14, 16, 18, 20. Ask: *What comes after 20; before 14? Why? What do the numbers all have in common? What other numbers are in this sequence? Say a number that is greater than 50, which is in this sequence. How do you know it is in the sequence?*

By the end of the lesson the children should be able to describe and extend number sequences and identify odd and even numbers. They should also know the following facts:
● When counting in steps of ten only the tens digit changes.
● When counting in steps of two, the units digit is always odd or even depending on whether your starting number is odd or even.

Number snake

How to play:

◗ Put your counter on zero and spin the spinner.

◗ Whatever it lands on, count on from zero until you reach that number on the line. Then, on paper, write down the next three numbers in the sequence. Ask your partner to check your sequence.

◗ Let Player 2 take a turn. Continue playing until you reach the end of the board.

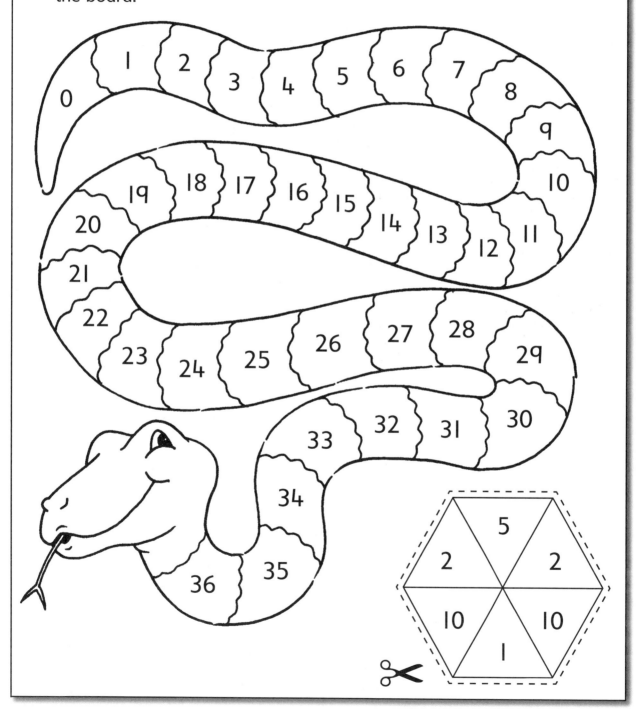

Measuring up

Key objective:
Read a simple scale to the nearest labelled division, including using a ruler to draw and measure lines to the nearest centimetre.

What you need
● Transparent 30cm ruler; a copy of activity sheet 'Measuring up' for each child; OHT of a jug and scales; blank OHT; OHP; individual whiteboards; paper and pens.

Further support
For measurements using a ruler, give extra support to less confident pupils by working with them yourself or asking a teaching assistant to work with them. Support the children's own work or, if necessary, be the child's 'hands' following the child's precise instructions as to where to place the ruler. Encourage the child to read the measurements.

Oral and mental starter
Put the ruler on the OHP and remind the children about reading scales and measuring lines. Ask for important tips when measuring the length of something using a ruler, for example, starting at zero, making sure the ruler follows the line, reading the scale carefully and so on.

Draw lines on the board and ask volunteers to demonstrate how to measure them to the nearest centimetre. Ask the rest of the class to write down estimates of the lengths of these lines and then to work out the difference between their estimate and the actual lengths.

Main assessment activity
Discuss other areas of measurement and the different ways to measure, for example, jugs for capacity and scales for mass. Show an OHT of a jug (see below) and draw arrows to show exact litres and half litres, and the marks in between. For each arrow ask the children to write the measurement either exactly or to the nearest half litre and show you. Ask the children to explain how they worked out their answer. Together with your observations from the oral and mental starter, you will be able to judge whether the children have achieved the objective.

Explain that the 'Measuring up' sheet requires the children to measure length, capacity and mass. Stress that they need to read the measurements carefully because some will be exact and others will need to be read to the nearest unit. Tell them that they need to use the words *exactly*, *nearly* and *just over* as appropriate.
While they are completing the sheet, ask individuals probing questions:
● *Why must you start at zero when you measure the length?*
● *How much water would be in here?*
● *How would you know if you weighed just over 2kg of potatoes?*

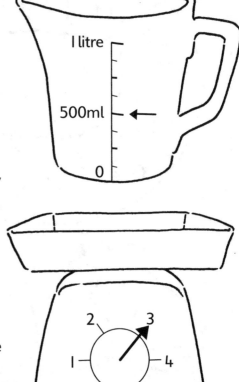

Plenary
Review how the children tackled the sheet and discuss how easily they were able to read measurements on the jug and weighing scales, and using a ruler (lining up the zero at one end of a line and making sure the ruler follows it). Ask: *How did you decide how long the line was in centimetres?* Ask the children to work with a partner to discuss the different measures they have thought about and the important things to remember when measuring using a ruler, jug, and scales.

Name   Date

Measuring up

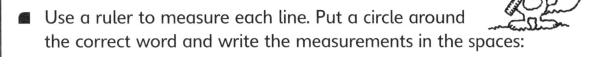

◣ Use a ruler to measure each line. Put a circle around the correct word and write the measurements in the spaces:

_____

just over, nearly, exactly _____ cm.

_____

just over, nearly, exactly _____ cm.

_____

just over, nearly, exactly _____ cm.

_____

just over, nearly, exactly _____ cm.

_____

just over, nearly, exactly _____ cm.

◣ Read the measurements on each of these scales and write what you think they are in the boxes.

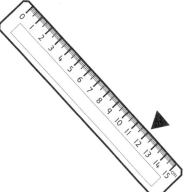

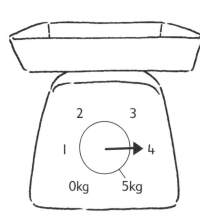

This measurement is

_____

This measurement is

_____

This measurement is

_____

Spider charts

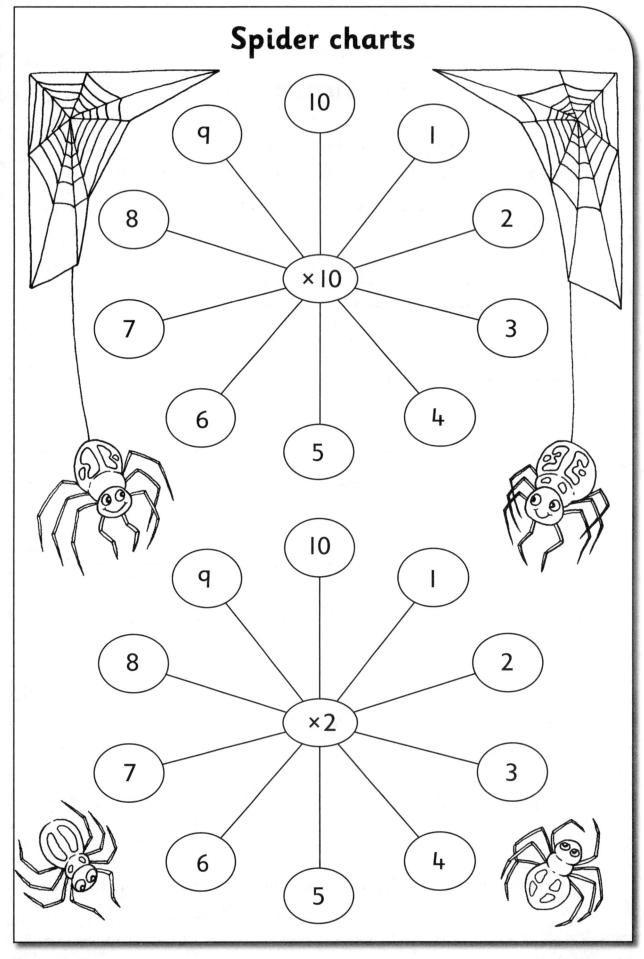

WEEK 14 📖 Half-term assessment

Name		Date

Assessment 3

1. Fill in the missing numbers

3	4	5	6	7					12

27	26	25	24	23	22				

24	34	44					94

15			45	55			85

89			59	49	39		

◼ Read the problems below and answer the questions showing how you worked them out.

2. Simone has a 10p in her money box. Sally gives her six more 10p pieces. How much money does she have now?

	Show how you worked this out

Ellie had 25 stickers. She bought another 25. How many has she got now?

	Show how you worked this out

Jamie collects marbles. He has 12. He puts them into groups of 6. How many marbles are in each group?

	Show how you worked this out

Name _____   Date _____

Assessment 4

1. Look at this:

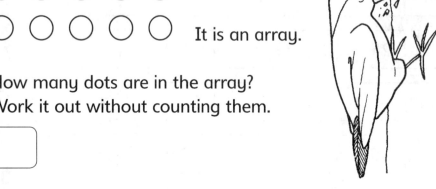

○ ○ ○ ○ ○

○ ○ ○ ○ ○   It is an array.

◀ How many dots are in the array?
◀ Work it out without counting them.

◀ Write a number sentence using × to show how many there are:

◀ Write a number sentence using + to show how many there are:

2. Look at these numbers:

23   13   31   32   46   16   61   27   72

◀ Write them in the correct circles:

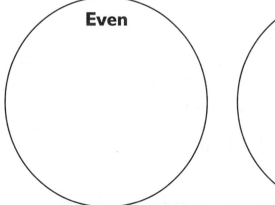

Even

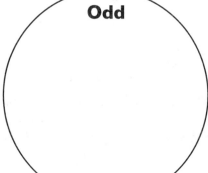

Odd

Assess and Review

Key objectives to be assessed
Assessment Lesson 1: Count, read, write and order whole numbers to at least 100. Know what each digit in a two-digit number represents, including zero as a place holder.
Assessment Lesson 2: Use mathematical vocabulary to describe position, direction and movement.

Photocopiable pages
Solve it! (p103); Where is it? (p105); Instruction cards for Lesson 1 (p106); Assessment test (p107-108).

Equipment
Individual whiteboards and pens; 2-digit number cards; single digit cards; length of string, wool or ribbon about 2m long; ruler; metre stick; plastic bag containing between 1-2kg of sand; weighing scales; container with between 1-2 litres of coloured water; measuring jug; large cube and compare bear; shapes: cube, cuboid, pyramid, sphere, cone, cylinder.

Assessment Activities

Mental maths assessment

1. Describe and extend simple number sentences a
Show a two-digit number card and ask the children to first write down the ten numbers that follow it and then preceded it. Together, count on in tens from 20 and 46 and back from 90 and 73.
Probing questions
● *If you count in ones from 27 to 35, how many ones will you count?*
● *If we start on 92 and count back in tens, how many tens is it till we say 12?*

2. Know addition and subtraction facts for numbers to at least ten f
Show the children a number card from five to ten. Ask them to write down all of the addition and subtraction facts for that number. Write a number sentence with blanks on the board, for example:

☐ + ◯ = 8

Probing question
● *What could the two missing numbers be?*

3. Know multiplication facts for the 2- and 10-times table k
Call out questions (eg 6 × 2) for the children to answer on their white board.
Probing question
● *What would you multiply by 2 to get 8?*

4. Recognise odd and even numbers b
Ask the children to write down an odd number between zero and ten, then an even number. Ask them to write a two-digit odd number and a two digit even number.
Probing questions
● *How do you know this is an odd/even number?*

Practical maths assessment
1. Compare lengths, masses and capacities m
2. Read a simple scale n
● Show the children a 15cm line on a piece of paper. Ask them to tell you how long they think it is, what equipment they could use to measure it, what units of measure they would use for this length and why. Finally ask them to measure it accurately.
● Repeat with a plastic bag filled with 1kg of sand.
● Repeat with a container that will hold 2 litres of coloured water.
● Ask the children to draw lines of 5cm, 10cm and 20cm on a piece of paper.
Probing questions
● *Can you draw a line between 5cm and 10cm?*

Written maths assessment
Give out copies of p107 and p108.
1. Choose strategies to solve problems l
Probing questions
● *Which of these can you work out in your head?*
● *How many different ways could you solve them?*

Solve It

Key objectives:
Know by heart all addition and subtraction facts for each number to at least 10; Choose and use appropriate operations and efficient calculation strategies to solve problems, explaining how the problem was solved.

What you need
● Numeral cards 0-10, a copy of activity sheet 'Solve it!' for each child; 0-10 number lines for less confident children.

Further support
Provide less confident children with 0-10 number lines or counting apparatus. If necessary read each problem to them.

Oral and mental starter
Rehearse the addition and subtraction facts for numbers to ten by asking the children to use numeral cards to show the answers to questions such as: *Show me two numbers with a total of 7.* Write all of their answers on the board in a systematic way to encourage logical thinking, for example: 0 + 7 = 7; 1 + 6 = 7. Repeat with different totals. Ask the children to show two numbers with a difference of five, again writing the subtraction sentences on the board.

Main assessment activity
Write this number sentence on the board: ? + ? = 9. Ask the children to make a number sentence from this, and find all of the possibie answers, for example: 0 + 9 = 9; 1 + 8 = 9; 2 + 7 = 9 and so on. Write all of their suggestions on the board. Repeat with a subtraction such as 9 - ? = ?. Tell the children that they will be working on number problems. Work through two examples:

1. *I had eight balloons, some were red and the others were blue. How many of each colour could I have?*
Discuss with the children all the possible solutions and write them as addition sentences, for example: 7 red + 1 blue = 8.

2. *I had eight balloons, some burst. How many could I have left?*
Again, discuss with the children all the possible solutions and write them as subtraction sentences.

Explain the 'Solve it!' activity sheet to the children. Tell them that they will need to write their answers as number sentences in the spaces provided, looking for all the possibilities. Sit with individuals to observe and question: *How do you know whether to add or to subtract? Are there any other solutions? Have you found them all? How do you know?*

Plenary
Review the children's work and try to identify how individual children solved each of the problems. To assess further, ask the children to make up problems involving number facts to ten and to talk these through with a partner. Check whether the children worked systematically to identify all the possibilities. By the end of the lesson the children should be able to tell you all the addition and subtraction facts to at least ten, demonstrate efficient calculation strategies for a range of problems and demonstrate their methods of working.

Name	Date

Solve it

◼ Write the answers to these problems as number sentences.

◼ Make sure that you find all the possible answers.

1. I bought a red ball and a blue ball.
They came to 10p in total.
How much could they each have cost?

2. There were seven robins in my garden.
Some of them flew away.
How many could be left?

3. There were eight marbles in my pocket.
Some were blue and some were green.
How many of each could there be?

4. I had 5p.
I spent some of it.
How much could I have left?

Coins © Crown Copyright, The Royal Mint

Where is it?

Key objective:
Use mathematical vocabulary to describe position, direction and movement.

What you need
● A copy of activity sheet 'Where is it?' for each child; vocabulary cards labelled: *clockwise quarter turn, anti-clockwise quarter turn, clockwise half turn, anti-clockwise half turn, clockwise whole turn, anti-clockwise whole turn* (from p106).

Further support
If there are children who have a problem remembering the positional words, give them visual clues, for example, an arrow pointing right and the word *right*. If necessary, read each instruction to the children.

Oral and mental starter
Ask the children to think of as many words associated with position, direction and movement as they can. Allow them to think, then ask them to share their ideas with a partner. Afterwards, join partners and share ideas as a group of four and then finally as a whole class. Write the vocabulary on the board in three columns one for position, one for direction and the last for movement.

Main assessment activity
Tell the children that during this part of the lesson they will be concentrating on direction and movement. Ask them to stand and pretend to be robots. They must stand still but turn in the directions you command. Hold up the vocabulary cards as you say: *Make a clockwise quarter turn, make an anti-clockwise half turn, now make a clockwise turn the size of a right angle. Where are you?* You should be back where you started. Repeat several times and then invite a few volunteers to take your role as 'commander'.

Show the children the 'Where is it?' activity sheet, which includes an outline picture of a tree on a hill with instructions to position a variety of objects or living things. The children must copy a drawing of each item in the correct position. For example, they should draw a cat in a space to the left of the tree, the flower to the right of the tree, the sun above the tree and so on. Use an acetate copy of the picture to model one or two examples.

Supervise some of the children and ask: *Which is your right hand? How can that help you to place the flower? What do we mean by centre? Can you think of another word that means the same thing?*

Plenary
By the end of the lesson the children should be able to explain the Year 2 vocabulary: *higher, lower, clockwise, anti-clockwise, quarter turn, right angle.* To check this, ask the children to make up sentences using one of these words, for example: *The hands on a clock move in a clockwise direction* or *In my picture the sun is higher in the sky than the butterfly.*

The children need to know all the relevant vocabulary for position, movement and direction, including each word's meaning. Again, you could check this by asking children to imagine and then describe a route around the class for a partner to follow.

SPRING

ASSESSMENT

Name   Date

Where is it?

Draw a cat on the left of the tree

Draw a bee next to the flower

Draw a ladybird lower than the apple on the tree

Draw a flower on the right of the tree

Draw a bird under the sun

Draw a bush at the bottom of the hill

Draw a dog in the middle of the hill

Draw a sun above the tree
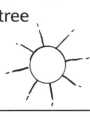

Draw an apple in the centre of the tree

Instruction words

Clockwise quarter turn

Anti-clockwise quarter turn

Clockwise half turn

Anti-clockwise half turn

Clockwise whole turn

Anti-clockwise whole turn

Clockwise right angled turn

Name   Date

Assessment 5

◀ Write down two ways of finding the answer to these calculations in the space provided.

1. | 6 + 7 + 9

2. | 27 + 35

3. | 49 – 26

4. | 6I – 5I

SPRING ASSESSMENT

Name

Date

Assessment 6

◢ Answer the following questions.

1. Samir has 15 grapes, Kantar has 13 and Cheryl has 7. How many do they have altogether?

Show how you worked this out.

2. Josh has 56p. He wants to buy a card. The card costs 11p more than he has. How much is the card?

Show how you worked this out.

3. Emily collects toy dinosaurs. She has 23 stegosaurus and 18 triceratops toys. How many does she have altogether?

Show how you worked this out.

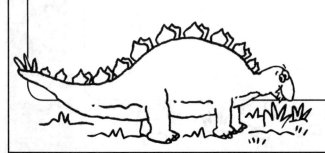

Assess and Review

Key objectives to be assessed
Assessment Lesson 1:
● **Understand that subtraction is the inverse of addition; state the subtraction corresponding to a given addition and vice versa.**
● **Choose and use appropriate operations and efficient calculation strategies to solve problems, explaining how each problem was solved.**
Assessment Lesson 2: **Understand the operation of multiplication as repeated addition or as describing an array.**

Photocopiable pages
Opposite operations (p111); Multiple dots (p103); Arrays (p114); Assessment test

(p115-116).
Equipment
Individual whiteboards and pens.

Assessment Activities

Mental maths assessment
1. Read and write whole numbers to at least 100 c
Check that the children can write on their whiteboards the numbers that you call out. Ensure that you include a variety of random single and two-digit numbers up to 100, including the 'teens' numbers, for example: 4, 78, 87, 40, 15.
Probing questions
● *How do you know that is fifteen and not fifty?*
● *Which number is this – 8 from 87? (They should say 80 not 8.)*

2. Know by heart multiplication facts for the 2 and 10 times tables k
Call out a mixture of incomplete multiplication facts, for example: *2 × 4 (say two times four); 2 × 9; something × 6 is 12; 10 × something is 70; 10 × 5.* As part of the assessment, notice whether the children actually know the facts instantly or whether they are counting in multiples and using their fingers.
Probing questions
● *How do you know that is the answer?*
● *If ? × ? = 20, what could the two missing numbers be?*

3. Describe and extend simple number sequences a
Say: *I have a secret number sequence. It has got these numbers in it: 6, 9, 12, 15. Write down the next two numbers in my sequence.* Repeat with simple sequences in fours and fives.

Probing questions
● *How did you know that those were the next numbers?*
● *Can you tell me the number that will go before my first number?*

Practical maths assessment
1. Read a simple scale n
Work through the following three activities with a small group of children:
● Draw a line ten centimetres long. Ask the children to measure it accurately.
● Put a bag of sand weighing one and a half kg into weighing scales. Ask the children to read the scale and tell you how heavy the bag is.
● Put one litre of coloured water in a measuring jug. Ask the children to read the scale and tell you how much is in the jug.
Probing questions
● *Tell me some important tips to remember when measuring something with a ruler.*
● *What would happen if you did not start measuring from zero on the ruler?*

Written maths assessment
Give out copies of the Assessment test on p115 and p116.
1. Know by heart all addition and subtraction facts for each number to at least 10 f
● *How many possible answers are there to this?*
2. Order whole numbers to at least 100 c
● *What number could go in between these numbers?*

Opposite operations

Key objectives:
● Understand that subtraction is the inverse of addition; state the subtraction corresponding to a given addition and vice versa.
● Choose and use appropriate operations and efficient calculation strategies to solve problems, explaining how each problem was solved.

What you need
● Whiteboards; paper and pens; enlarged number grid taken from 'Opposite operations' sheet, copied on to an OHT; a copy of activity sheet 'Opposite operations' for each child.

Further support
Provide less confident children with a number line or hundred square to assist them with calculating the additions and subtractions. If necessary help them by scribing the problems for them.

Oral and mental starter

Ask the children to tell you all they can about addition and subtraction, in particular draw out the fact that subtraction is the inverse (opposite) of addition. On the board write 14, 12, 26, and ask the children to use these numbers to write two addition and two subtraction sentences. Use a number line to demonstrate the link for example:

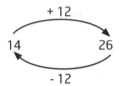

Repeat with other examples.

Main assessment activity

Show the children the OHT. Explain that they need to pick two numbers and make two addition number sentences and then, using their answer, they need to make two subtraction number sentences. For example, if they pick 25 and 36, the number sentences would be: 25 + 36 = 61; 36 + 25 = 61; 61 - 25 = 36 and 61 - 36 = 25. Allow time for the children to think first, discuss with a partner, write their number sentences and finally share with the rest of the class.

Encourage the children to select numbers from the number grid to write addition and subtraction number sentences. After they have made their sentences, they should put them into a problem context to share with the rest of the class during the plenary. Model the activity precisely:
I am going to choose 30 and 21, and make a subtraction sentence: 30 - 21 = 9. My second subtraction using these numbers would be 30 - 9 = 21. I can make up two addition sentences: 9 + 21 = 30 and 21 + 9 = 30. I am now thinking of a number, if I take away 21, I am left with 9. What is my number?

Sit with pairs of children to observe, asking such questions as: *What addition facts can you use to help you calculate 12 - 8 and 19 - 8?* Explain how they helped you.

Plenary

By the end of the lesson the children should know that addition and subtraction are inverse operations. Say to the class: *I am thinking of a number. If I add 36 I will get 41. What is my number? I am thinking of a number. If I take away four, I am left with ten. What is my number? How do you know?*

Invite volunteers, particularly those you wish to assess, to ask similar questions. As they do, ask the class to explain how they can work them out and write appropriate calculations on the board.

Opposite operations

■ Pick two numbers from the grid below. Make up two addition and one subtraction number sentences, then make up an 'I am thinking of a number' problem.

12	16	23	25
10	5	28	8
30	14	36	21

My two numbers are: My subtraction sentence:

My addition sentences: My problem:

My two numbers are: My subtraction sentence:

My addition sentences: My problem:

My two numbers are: My subtraction sentence:

My addition sentences: My problem:

Multiple dots

Key objective:
Understand the operation of multiplication as repeated addition or as describing an array.

What you need
● Set of cards from the 'Multiple dots' sheet for each pair of children; whiteboards or paper and pens.

Further support
Ask the less confident children to write or draw one way of describing only. For children who are still struggling, make the activity a matching task, where they match visual array cards with number sentence cards.

Oral and mental starter

Remind the children about multiplication as repeated addition and describing arrays. Count in twos, fives and tens, using fingers. Begin in tens from zero. At the first count (ten) put up one finger, at the second another finger (20) and so on to 100. Stop the children a couple of times during each count and ask: *How many fingers am I holding up? How many lots of ten is that? Who can write that as a number sentence?* 10 + 10 + 10 = 30. *Is there another way to write this?* 10 × 3 = 30. Repeat this for twos and fives.

Main assessment activity

Show the children an array of 20 dots made up from two rows of ten dots. Demonstrate two lots of ten and ten lots of two.

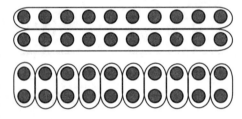

Ask the children to think first and then tell a partner how to write these as number sentences, for example: 10 + 10 = 20; 10 × 2 = 20; 2 + 2 + 2 + 2 + 2 + 2 + 2 + 2 + 2 + 2 = 20 and 2 × 10 = 20.

Ask: *Can you record in a different way* (such as a four by five array)? An answer to this will be a good indication that the children have achieved the lesson's objective.

Give each pair of children a pile of cards from the photocpiable sheet. The cards show either arrays or repeated addition statements. The idea is that the children take turns to pick a card from a pile, draw it and write the other way of describing it on a separate piece of paper. For example, if they pick an array card, they draw it, write the repeated addition and finally write the total number of dots. They should do the same for the cards that include repeated addition statements.

While they are doing this, sit with pairs of children and ask probing questions such as: *How can you work out the number of dots without counting? What number sentence can you write using the × symbol? What about the + symbol? Can you tell me how we could make equal rows for 30 dots?*

Plenary

By the end of the lesson the children should be able to describe multiplications as arrays and repeated additions and understand that multiplications can be written using both the × and + symbols. Ask the whole class how they could arrange 12 dots in equal rows and record with a number sentence. Repeat with 20 dots and then 24.

Multiple dots

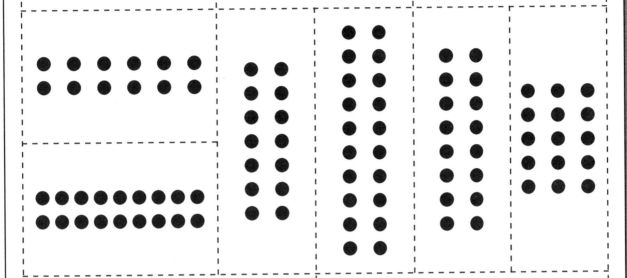

10 + 10	10 + 10 + 10
10 + 10 + 10 + 10	2 + 2 + 2
2 + 2 + 2 + 2	2 + 2 + 2 + 2 + 2
5 + 5 + 5	5 + 5 + 5 + 5
5 + 5 + 5 + 5 + 5 + 5	

www.scholastic.co.uk   ALL NEW 100 MATHS HOMEWORK AND ASSESSMENT · YEAR 2

SPRING ASSESSMENT

Arrays

1.

2.

3.
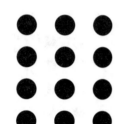

4.
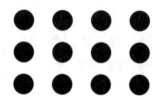

5.

6.
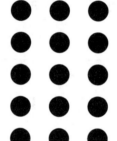

7.

Name

Date

Assessment 7

◢ Fill in the missing numbers in these number sentences.

◢ Use different numbers each time.

1. ☐ + ◯ = 6

2. ☐ + ◯ = 6

3. ☐ + ◯ = 6

4. ☐ + ◯ = 6

5. 8 = ◯ + ☐

6. 8 = ◯ + ☐

7. 8 = ◯ + ☐

8. 8 = ◯ + ☐

Name   Date

Assessment 8

◗ Use these numbers to make four or more two-digit numbers.

| 4 | 6 | 1 |

Write your numbers here

◗ Now order them on this line

Lowest   Highest

◗ Repeat with these numbers

| 2 | 5 | 7 |

Write your numbers here

◗ Now order them on this line

Lowest   Highest

◗ Repeat with these numbers

| 0 | 8 | 3 |

Write your numbers here

◗ Now order them on this line

Lowest   Highest

PHOTOCOPIABLE

Assess and Review

Key objectives to be assessed

Assessment Lesson 1:

- **Know by heart all addition and subtraction facts for each number to at least 10.**
- **Choose and use appropriate operations and efficient calculation strategies to solve problems, explaining how the problem was solved.**

Assessment Lesson 2: **Estimate, measure and compare lengths, masses and capacities, using standard units; suggest units and equipment for such measurements.**

Photocopiable pages

Up the hill (p119); Made to measure (p120); Statement cards (p120); Assessment test (p123-124).

Equipment

Individual whiteboards and pens; 10cm piece of wool; ruler; plastic bag containing 500g of sweets; 1 kg weight; weighing scales; container with 1 ½ litres of coloured water; measuring jug.

Assessment Activities

Mental maths assessment

1. State the subtraction corresponding to a given addition and vice versa h

Show number sentences, ask the children to write down the corresponding addition or subtraction eg show 18 + 17 = 35, they write 35 – 17 = 18

Probing questions

- *I thought of a number, added 19 and got a total of 30. What was my number?*

2. Know by heart facts for the 2- and 10- times tables k

Hold up number cards from zero to ten and ask the children to write down the answer when multiplied by two or ten.

Probing questions

- *What two numbers could be multiplied together to make 18? How do you know?*

3. Recognise odd and even numbers b

Ask the children to write down single-digit and then two-digit odd and even numbers.

Probing questions

- *How do you know this is an odd/even number?*

4. Know all addition and subtraction facts for each number up to at least 10 f

Write the number ten and ask the children to write down all of its addition and subtraction facts.

Probing question

- *X + Y = 10. Can you tell me some number facts that fit this?*

Practical maths assessment

1. Estimate, measure then compare lengths, masses and capacities m
2. Read a simple scale n

Show the children a 10cm piece of wool. Ask how long they think it is, what equipment they could use to measure it and what units of measure they would use. Ask them to measure it accurately and say how close their estimate was.

Repeat with a bag filled with 500g of sweets. Let the children feel a 1kg weight as a guide.

Repeat with a jug with 1½ litres of coloured water.

Probing question

- *Can you tell me something that is a) longer/ shorter b) lighter/heavier c) less/more full?*

Written maths assessment

Give out copies of the Assessment test on p123 and p124.

1. Describe and extend number sequences a

- *I have 20 in my sequence what am I counting in?*

2. Order whole numbers to at least 100 c

- *What clues did you look for to order? Why?*

3. Understand subtraction as the inverse of addition e

- *Can you show this using 12, 17 and 39?*

4. Use mathematical vocabulary to describe position, direction and movement p

- *Can you tell me how to get to the door if I move in straight lines? Is there another way?*

Up the hill

Key objective:
● **Count, read, write and order whole numbers to at least 100.**
● **Know what each digit in a two-digit number represents, including zero as a place holder.**

What you need
● A copy of activity sheet 'Up the hill' for each pair of children; sets of numeral cards from 1–99; pendulum (three cubes attached to a piece of string); Blu-tack; partitioning cards.

Further support
Allow less confident children to use a 100 square for additional support. If numbers to 100 prove too difficult, give them number cards from 10–30 or 1–20 and a number line.

Oral and mental starter

Hold up a number card and count on in ones to the swing of the pendulum. Repeat a few times. Show the children two random number cards and ask them to read each card. Fix these numbers to the board, with the smallest number first. Pick five more cards and ask volunteers to position all seven numbers in the correct order, moving them around when necessary. Ask: *Which is the smallest number? How do you know? What clues did you look for?*

Main assessment activity

Keep the ordered cards on the board. Select appropriate partitioning cards for the seven numbers, for example, 20 and 5 for 25. For each one in turn, invite the children to choose partitioning cards and write the matching number sentence on the board: 25 = 20 + 5.
Ask: *Why has 20 a zero at the end? What would the number be without it?*

Give each pair of children a copy of the 'Up the hill' activity sheet and 20 numeral cards from 10–99. Tell the children to place the cards face down in a pack, take turns to pick one and tell their partner what it is. If, for example, they pick 53, they should say the number and then write the number sentence: 53 = 50 + 3. Repeat until they have written ten number sentences between them on their sheet. They should now order their numbers in the squares with the smallest at the bottom of the hill.

Sit with pairs of children and ask probing questions such as: *What is the same/ different about these cards? How did you know it was bigger than that one? What clues did you look for? Tell me a number that comes in between these two numbers.*

If any pairs complete this activity quickly and confidently, ask them to repeat it using three-digit cards to make up three-digit numbers.

Plenary

Question the whole class about ordering numbers, asking them to explain to each other in pairs what they would look at to give clues (for example, tens digit, then units digit). This activity will give an indication of the children's level of understanding of place value. By the end of the lesson the children should know with confidence what each digit in a number represents, that zero is a place holder and that when ordering numbers they need to look at the most significant digit first.

Name

Date

Up the hill

◢ Write your number sentences here.

◢ Now order your numbers on the hill, smallest at the bottom.

Made to measure

Oral and mental starter

Begin the lesson by asking questions about length, mass and capacity. For example: *What unit would I use to weigh a bag of potatoes? What equipment would I use to measure your height?* In pairs, encourage the children to think of the unit or equipment that would match your statement, write it down and show you. Ask: *Why can we not use x unit? What would that be used for? Why could we not use x equipment? What would that equipment be used to measure?*

Main assessment activity

You might wish to tackle the three activities as a whole class or in pairs within three groups, with each group rotating after about ten minutes.

Activity 1
Length: Encourage each pair of children to make four worms out of plasticine. Ask them to place them on the table in order from shortest to longest, estimate their lengths, measure them to the nearest centimetre and record the answers on their sheet.

Activity 2
Mass: Challenge each pair of children to find four objects, two of which they estimate to be less than 1kg in weight and two to be more. Ask them to place them on the table in order from lightest to heaviest, weigh them on pan scales against a 1kg weight or on a set of household scales and record the results on their sheet.

Activity 3
Capacity: Ask each pair of children to find four containers, two of which they estimate will hold less than 1 litre of water and two that they estimate will hold more. Encourage them to measure a litre of water and test their estimations, again recording the outcomes.

Observe the activities and ask probing questions: *How long do you think your worm is? How can you find out? What equipment could you use to measure it? Tell me the units that would be suitable. If your worm was really, really long, what could you use instead of centimetres and a ruler?*

Plenary

By the end of the lesson the children should know that length is measured in centimetres and metres, with a ruler, metre stick or tape measure. They should know that mass is measured in kilograms with a set of scales and that capacity is measured in litres using a measuring jug. They should be able to practically estimate, measure and compare lengths, masses and capacities.

Ask the children to tell you about the units they used and why they used particular apparatus. Ask: *Tell me some units that would/would not be suitable for each activity?*

Name	Date

 # Made to measure

Length

My worms	Estimate	Measurement	Difference
Worm 1			
Worm 2			
Worm 3			
Worm 4			

Mass

Object	Estimate More or less than 1kg?	Measurement More or less than 1kg?	Right or wrong?

Capacity

Object	Estimate More or less than 1 litre?	Measurement More or less than 1 litre?	Right or wrong?

SUMMER ASSESSMENT

Vocabulary cards

◢ Copy and cut out the vocabulary cards. Give a set to each group of children.

◢ In what unit would I weigh a bag of potatoes?

◢ What equipment would I use to weigh myself?

◢ What equipment would I use to measure your height?

◢ What unit would I use to measure the height of this building?

◢ What units would I use to measure the length of this pencil?

◢ What equipment would I use to measure the length of your book?

◢ What unit would I use to measure the amount of water in my bath?

◢ What equipment would I use for measuring how much juice is in the bottle?

centimetres	metres
litres	kilograms
ruler	metre stick
jug	scales

Assessment 9

1. Here are different parts of some number sequences that you know well. See if you can finish each one.

10	12	14	16				

100	90		70			40	30

12		18	21			30

45	40			25	20	

16	20		28		36

2. Put these numbers in the correct order on the line.

45	82	2	14	66	50

Smallest _____ Largest

3. Use these numbers to make up two addition and two subtraction number sentences.

12	5	7

Name _____ Date _____

Assessment 10

◼ Here are two problems for you to work out. Write your answer in the space under each problem and show how you worked them out in the box beside the space.

1. Samir has 16 books, Matt has 18, Poppy has 14 and Hanni has 12.
How many do they have altogether?

> Tell me how you will solve this problem.

> Show how you worked this out.

2. Robbie had £1.50. He bought a bag of sweets which cost 50p and a drink which cost 70p. How much did he have left?

> Tell me how you will solve this problem.

> Show how you worked this out.

ALL NEW 100 MATHS HOMEWORK AND ASSESSMENT · YEAR 2   www.scholastic.co.uk

Assess and Review

Key objectives to be assessed

Assessment Lesson 1:
- **Know and use halving as the inverse of doubling.**
- **Choose and use appropriate operations and efficient calculation strategies to solve problems, explaining how the problem was solved.**

Assessment Lesson 2:
- **Know by heart multiplication facts for the 2- and 10-times tables.**
- **Choose and use appropriate operations and efficient calculation strategies to solve problems, explaining how each problem was solved.**

Photocopiable pages
Doubles and halves (p127); Multiplication triangles (p129); Missing number cards (p130); Assessment test (p131-132).

Equipment
Interlocking cubes; ruler; rice; weighing scales; cups; measuring jug.

Assessment Activities

Mental maths assessment

1. Know by heart all addition and subtraction facts for each number to at least 10 ⬛f
Ask the children to fill in the numbers on the 'Missing number cards' (p130), explaining that the numbers in the circles must be ten or less.

Probing questions
- *Can you show me all the pairs that make nine?*
- *Can you show me pairs of numbers that have a difference of three?*

2. Recognise odd and even numbers ⬛b
Give each child a handful of interlocking cubes.

Probing questions
- *Can you use these to make two equal towers? How many different equal towers can you make?*
- *Can you use these to make two unequal towers? Are these odd or even?*

3. State the subtraction corresponding to a given addition and vice versa ⬛h
Write on the board: 12 + 5 = 17.

Probing questions
- *If you know that 12 + 5 = 17, what else do you know?*
- *How can you check without calculating?*

Practical maths assessment

1. Estimate, measure then compare lengths, masses and capacities using standard units; suggest suitable units and equipment for such measurements ⬛m

2. Read a simple scale to the nearest labelled division, including using a ruler to draw and measure lines to the nearest centimetre ⬛n
Ask the children to do the following:
- Draw an estimated line of 20cm, then measure it.
- Estimate how many cups of water will make a litre and then find out.
- Collect an amount of rice that you think will weigh close to ½ kg and weigh it.

Probing questions
- *What can you use to check to see whether you are right or not?*
- *Was your estimate close?*

Written maths assessment
Distribute the Assessment test on p131 and p132.

1. Order whole numbers to at least 100 ⬛c
- *Which number will go at the end? Why?*
- *Which numbers will you look at to say which is the greatest out of 32 and 41? Why?*

2. Understand subtraction as the inverse of addition ⬛e
- *If you know that 16 - 5 = 11, what would add to 11 to get 16? Explain why you think this.*

3. Know and use halving as the inverse of doubling ⬛j
- *What do we mean by doubling? How do we double a number?*
- *What do we mean by halving? How do we halve a number?*

Doubles and halves

Key objective:
● **Know and use halving as the inverse of doubling.**
● **Choose and use appropriate operations and efficient calculation strategies to solve problems, explaining how the problem was solved.**

What you need
● Several sets of numeral cards showing: numbers from 0 -10, even numbers from 11- 20 and multiples of ten to 100; spinners (divided into five sections, two marked 'halve it', two marked 'double it' and one marked 'miss a turn'); whiteboards or paper and pens; a copy of activity sheet 'Doubles and halves' and different coloured counters for each pair of children.

Further support
Ask adult helpers to support the activity, listening to what is said and assisting with recording.

Oral and mental starter

Write the words *Double*, *Doubling*, *Half* and *Halving* on the board. Give the children some thinking time to come up with an explanation of these terms. Let them practise their explanation with a partner and then share it with the rest of the class. Call out suitable random numbers up to 100 for the children to double and halve. Ask them to show their answers using digit cards.

Main assessment activity

Write the following on the board: *Double 4 = 8 so half of 8 = 4*. From this, ask what is special about doubling and halving. Lead towards the fact that halving is the inverse (opposite) of doubling.

Ask questions, for example: *If we know that double 12 is 24, what else do we know?* Repeat using half. Say: *If we know that half ten is five, what else do we know?* (The children should write *double 5 = 10*.) Ask: *I am thinking of a number. I halved it and got four. What number was I thinking of? How did you work that out?*

Give each pair of children a copy of 'Doubles and halves' game sheet. Encourage them to place the numeral cards in a pile, face down, in front of them. The first player picks a card, spins the spinner and carries out the instruction as indicated by the spinner ('halve it' or 'double it'). If the player is successful at doubling or halving the number they move one space closer to the dartboard. The second player does exactly the same. If the players cannot work out the answer or spin 'miss a turn' they must wait until their next go. Encourage them to record their work to show the relationship between doubling and halving. The first player to reach the dartboard is the winner. Observe the pairs and ask probing questions such as: *How do you know double 12 is 24? Can you explain how you can use this fact to say what half 24 is?*

Plenary

By the end of the lesson the children should recognise that halving is the inverse of doubling. Ask some questions to put this into a real life context, inviting children to explain their solutions, for example: *I have some money. My friend has double the amount, she has 40p. How much do I have? How do you know? Pardeep has some money. Sam has half the amount, she has 15p. How much does Pardeep have? How do you know?*

Doubles and halves

Multiplication triangles

Key objective:
● **Know by heart multiplication facts for the 2- and 10-times tables.**
● **Choose and use appropriate operations and efficient calculation strategies to solve problems, explaining how each problem was solved.**

What you need
● Pendulum (three cubes attached to a piece of string); whiteboards or paper and pens; a copy of activity sheet 'Multiplication triangles' for each child.

Further support
Provide less confident children with a list of two- and ten-times tables facts. Try jumbling up the facts on each list, so that they still need to identify the answers.

Oral and mental starter

Rehearse the two- and ten-times tables facts using the pendulum. As it swings one-way call out a number from zero to ten, as it swings the other way, ask the children to call out the answer when it is multiplied by two. Repeat this for the ten-times table.

Main assessment activity

Write this missing number sentence on the board:
$? \times ? = 20$. Ask the children to tell you which numbers are needed to make this sentence correct. Remind them that the two and ten-times tables might help. Aim towards: $10 \times 2 = 20$ and $2 \times 10 = 20$. *Can you think of any others?* Say: *I am thinking of a number, if I multiply it by ten I will get 60. What is my number? How do you know? I am thinking of a number, if I multiply it by four I will get eight. What is my number? How do you know?*

Give each child a copy of the 'Multiplication triangles' sheet. The sheet requires them to complete a triangle that links the three numbers in a multiplication statement. Demonstrate exactly what the children should do using an OHT of the activity sheet. Explain that they need to work out what number goes in the missing circle to create a triangle where the bottom two numbers multiply to make the top number. After they have worked out each number, they should write two multiplication facts in the rectangle alongside.
Sit with individual children and ask probing questions such as: *How are you going to find the missing number? Which other numbers make a multiplication with the same answer?* When they have completed the task, ask them to make up more triangles on the back of the sheet.

Plenary

Invite volunteers to describe their multiplication triangles. Ask them to explain exactly how they knew what the missing numbers were. Once they have told you, ask them how they could check. For example: I know that 3 should go there because $3 \times 10 = 30$. I can check by counting ten, three times.
This links with the Key objective of understanding multiplication as repeated addition. By the end of the lesson the children should know the two and ten times tables facts by heart and with quick recall.

WEEK 14 LESSON 2 🪧 End-of-term assessment

Name	Date

Multiplication triangles

◢ Fill in the circle with the correct number to make a multiplication.
When you have, write two multiplication facts in the rectangle. One
has been done for you.

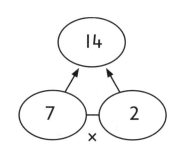

Multiplication Facts:
7 x 2 = 14
2 x 7 = 14

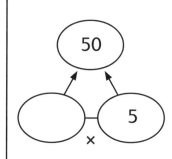

Multiplication Facts:

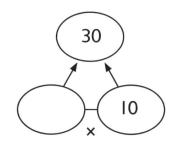

Multiplication Facts:

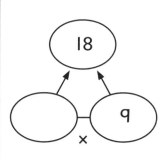

Multiplication Facts:

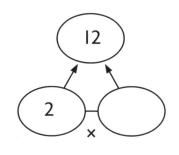

Multiplication Facts:

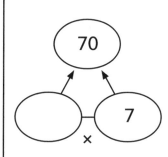

Multiplication Facts:

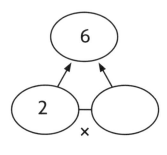

Multiplication Facts:

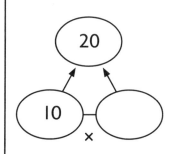

Multiplication Facts:

Missing number cards

■ Complete each number sentence by filling in the missing numbers. Remember that the number in each circle must be less than ten. Make up some more number sentences with different numbers in the squares.

$$\square + 3 = \bigcirc$$

$$\square + 6 = \bigcirc$$

$$7 + \square = \bigcirc$$

$$2 + \square = \bigcirc$$

$$4 - \square = \bigcirc$$

$$12 - \square = \bigcirc$$

$$\square - 5 = \bigcirc$$

$$\square - 4 = \bigcirc$$

ALL NEW 100 MATHS HOMEWORK AND ASSESSMENT • YEAR 2

www.scholastic.co.uk

SUMMER ASSESSMENT

Name	Date

Assessment 11

1. Write these numbers in the boxes in order, from smallest to greatest.

27	95	3	18	56

Smallest   Greatest

Write a number that could go in the two empty boxes.

15	20			35

2. You know that 12 + 3 = 15, so use this knowledge to complete the following number sentences.

You know that 20 – 16 = 4, so use this knowledge to complete the following number sentences.

a. ☐ + 12 = 15   f. ☐ – 4 = 16

b. ☐ – 12 = 3   g. ☐ – 16 = 4

c. ☐ – 3 = 12   h. ☐ + 16 = 20

d. 15 – ☐ = 12   i. 20 – ☐ = 16

e. 12 + ☐ = 15   j. 4 + ☐ = 20

SUMMER ASSESSMENT

Name   Date

Assessment 12

1. Double these numbers.

a. | 10 | → | |

b. | 8 | → | |

c. | 15 | → | |

d. | 13 | → | |

e. | 9 | → | |

2. Halve these numbers.

a. | 14 | → | |

b. | 20 | → | |

c. | 10 | → | |

d. | 6 | → | |

e. | 16 | → | |

3. Fill in these 'life cycles'. You can choose your own starting numbers.

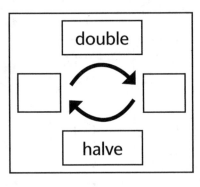

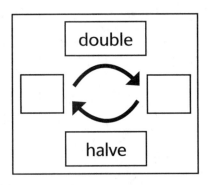

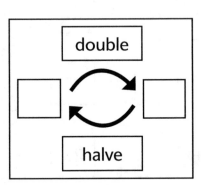

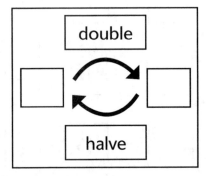

www.scholastic.co.uk

Assess and Review

Photocopiable pages
Mental maths tests (p134-137); Assessment test (p138-140).

Equipment
One- and two-digit number cards; whiteboards and pens; 10cm strips of paper; a metre stick; 1kg bag of sugar; weighing scales; 1 litre bottle filled with coloured water; various waterproof containers; a measuring jug.

Mental maths assessment
Mental maths tasks
Provide each child with a copy of recording sheet 1 (Term 1) on page 135 or recording sheet 2 (Term 2) on page 137. Read the instructions on pages 134 and 136 before commencing the tests.

1. c d
Give each child five two-digit number cards. Ask them to read each card aloud, then order them.
Probing questions
- *How are these numbers different/the same?*
- *Why is the zero in 306 important?*

2. k
Call out numbers to ten. Challenge the children to quickly multiply the numbers by two and then ten.
Probing question
- *If I have six stickers and Tom has ten times as many, how many does he have?*

3. g
Pick two cards to 15, and ask the children to add them together. Repeat with three cards.
Probing questions:
- *What different ways could we add 2, 12 and 6?*
- *Does it matter in which order we add numbers?*

Practical maths assessment
1. n
Work through the following activities.
- Show the children a 10cm strip of paper. Ask them to draw you a line that is a little longer and another a little shorter. Discuss their results.
- From a marked starting point, ask the children to walk a little further than the length of the metre stick and then a little less. Compare how far they walked with the metre stick.
- Ask the children to feel the weight of the bag of sugar and find something that they think weighs the same. Ask them to weigh their chosen object to see how close they are.
- Ask the children to pour one litre of water into the measuring jug. Then ask them to find a container that will hold the same amount. Were they correct?
Probing question
- *What do we mean by estimate?*

Written maths assessment
Give out copies of p138, 139 and 140.
1. f
Probing question
- *How do you know you have all of the addition and subtraction facts?*

2. a
3. b
Probing questions
- *I have the sequence: 12, 14, 16, 18. What comes before 12? How do you know it is an even number?*

4. e h
Probing questions
- *Write four number sentences using: 12, 30, 18?*
- *What addition facts can you use work out 12 - 8?*

5. l
Probing question
- *How could you arrange these 20 cubes in equal rows? Record your answer in a number sentence.*

6. j
Probing questions
- *I halved a number and got 14. What was my number? How do you know?*

7. i
Probing questions
- *I need to know the total of 15 + 16. How can I work it out?*

8. o
Probing question
- *What is the same about a hexagon and a pentagon?*

9. p
Probing question
- *Can you give me instructions so that I can walk from here to the door?*

🗀 **End-of-year assessment**

Mental maths test 1

This mental assessment includes ten questions, which can be given to the children towards the end of the school year.

Setting the test
Provide each child with a copy of the recording sheet for Test 1 (p135). Ask the children to write their names and the date on to the sheet. Explain what will happen: *I am going to ask you some questions. Work out the answers in your head and write the answer down on your sheet. I shall say each question twice and give you a little bit of thinking time.*

Say the question number, then the question twice with a short pause between repetitions. For Section A, give the children at least five seconds of thinking time, then move on to the next question. For Section B, give the children at least ten seconds of thinking time before moving on to the next question. Repeat questions at the end of the assessment as necessary. Answers are given in square brackets after each question.

Test 1

Section A

1. What is ten more than 24? [34]

2 Draw a circle around the multiples of five. [15 and 20]

3 I spend 20p. How much change will I get from 50p? [30p]

4 What is the difference between 28 and 32? [four]

5 What must I add to six to get ten? [four]

Section B

6. What is 13 + 19 [32]

7. Tick the circle that has $\frac{3}{4}$ shaded grey. [third circle]

8. Underline the month that comes after August. [September]

9. What is half of 30? [15]

10. How long is it from quarter past eight until nine o'clock? [45 minutes, $\frac{3}{4}$ of an hour]

Name	Date

Mental maths test 1 recording sheet

🗨 Listen to the questions then write your answers in the spaces provided.

1.	
2.	6 15 20 24
3.	
4.	
5.	
6.	
7.	
8.	July August September October November
9.	
10.	

Mental maths test 2

This mental assessment includes ten questions, which can be given to the children towards the end of the school year.

Provide each child with a copy of the recording sheet for Test 2 (p137). Ask the children to write their names and the date on to the sheet. Explain what will happen: *I am going to ask you some questions. Work out the answers in your head and write the answer down on your sheet. I shall say each question twice and give you a little bit of thinking time.*
Say the question number, then the question twice with a short pause between repetitions. For Section A, give the children at least five seconds of thinking time, then move on to the next question. For section B, give the children at least ten seconds of thinking time then move on to the next question. Repeat questions at the end of the assessment as necessary. Answers are given in square brackets after each question.

Test 2

Section A

1. What is ten less than 37? [27]

2. What is 18 plus nine? [27]

3. Circle the number of centimetres in a metre. [100]

4. What is half of 18? [nine]

5. What seven add eight? [15]

Section B

6. What is the difference between 27 and 42? [15]

7. Ten girls had four apples each. How many apples were there? [40]

8. Tick the shape on your sheet which is an octagon.

9. What is 13 + 7 + 10? [30]

10. I buy a toy dog for 25p and a toy cat for 24p. How much change do I get from 50p? [1p]

End-of-year assessment

Name	Date

Mental maths test 2 recording sheet

◀ Listen to the questions then write your answers in the spaces provided.

1.	
2.	
3.	50 100 150 200
4.	
5.	
6.	
7.	
8.	
9.	
10.	

🗎 **End-of-year assessment**

Name   Date

Check up 1

1. Write down all of the different ways to make each number in the box. For example: 5: 4+1; 3+2; 2+3; 1+4.

6

3

7

4

2. Write the next three numbers in this sequence.

37	47	57			

3. You know that 17 - 6 = 11, so use that knowledge to write the answers to these number sentences.

$\boxed{}$ + 6 = 17   17 - $\boxed{}$ = 6 $\boxed{}$ + 11 = 17

$\boxed{}$ – 11 = 6   11 + $\boxed{}$ = 17

4. We can describe 3 × 5 in different ways. For example: 3 × 5 and 5 x 3. Use repeated addition: 5 + 5 + 5 = 15.
Or as an array:

Describe 4 × 2 as repeated addition:

Describe 4 × 2 as an array:

Check up 2

5. Match these doubles and halves

double 6	half of 20
double 7	half of 8
double 9	half of 14
double 10	half of 12
double 20	half of 18
double 4	half of 40

6. Write your answer in the space under each problem and show how you worked it out in the box beside the space.

If a bike has two wheels, how many wheels will six bikes have altogether?

This is how I worked it out

There are five red sweets and four blue sweets in a bag. How many are there in ten bags?

This is how I worked it out

Sam had 50p, he bought a lolly for 10p and a bag of crisps for 35p. How much money did he have left?

This is how I worked it out

🔲 **End-of-year assessment**

Name   Date

Check up 3

7. Draw lines to match the labels to the shapes

| pentagon | circle | cube | cylinder | square | pyramid |

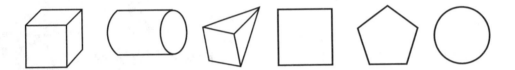

| rectangle | triangle | hexagon | cuboid | octagon | sphere |

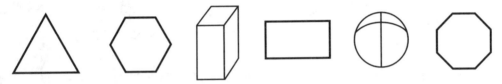

8. Write the correct word to match the position of the bear

Words to choose from

under   on top   behind   in front   beside

Class record sheet

Names

Key objectives: Year 2																
Describe and extend simple number sequences: count on or back in ones or tens, starting from any two-digit number																
Recognise odd and even numbers.																
Read, write and order whole numbers to at least 100.																
Know what each digit in a two-digit number represents, including zero as a place holder.																
Understand that subtraction is the inverse of addition.																
Know by heart all addition and subtraction facts for each number to at least ten.																
Use knowledge that addition can be done in any order to do mental calculations more efficiently.																
State the subtraction corresponding to a given addition and vice versa.																
Understand the operation of multiplication as repeated addition or as describing an array																
Know and use halving as the inverse of doubling.																
Know by heart multiplication facts for the 2- and 10-times																
Choose and use appropriate operations and efficient calculation strategies to solve problems, explaining how a problem was solved.																
Estimate, measure and compare lengths, masses and capacities, using standard units; suggest suitable units and equipment for such measurements.																
Read a simple scale to the nearest labelled division, including using a ruler to draw and measure lines to the																
Use the mathematical names for common 3D and 2D shapes. Sort and describe some of their features.																
Use mathematical vocabulary to describe position, direction and movement.																

Answer sheet

Autumn Term

P86 **Add them up** 6 + 10 + 6 = 22; 15 + 7 + 3 + 15 = 40; 12 + 13 - 25; 8 + 9 + 4 = 21; 15 + 13 + 5 = 33; 25 + 30 + 25 = 80; 19 + 7 + 3 = 29; 14 + 16 = 30; 13 + 13 + 14 = 40; 2 + 18 + 8 + 12 = 40.

P89 **What shape am I?** Square; Cylinder; Rectangle; Cube; Cone; Octagon; Triangle; Sphere.

P91 **Assessment 1** 1. 26; 2. 72; 3. 24

P92 **Assessment 2**

1.

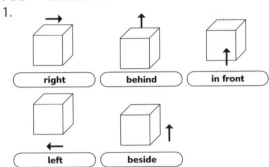

2.

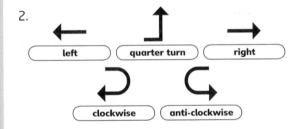

P95 **Number snake** Answers will vary.

P97 **Measuring up**

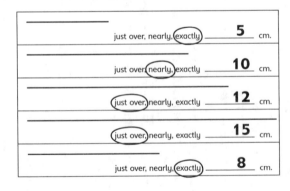

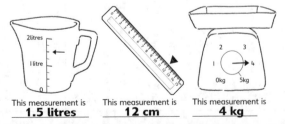

This measurement is **1.5 litres**   This measurement is **12 cm**   This measurement is **4 kg**

P99 **Assessment 3** 1.

3	4	5	6	7	**8**	**9**	**10**	**11**	12
27	26	25	24	23	22	**21**	**20**	**19**	**18**
24	34	44	**54**	**64**	**74**	**84**	94		
15	**25**	**35**	45	55	**65**	**75**	85		
89	**79**	**69**	59	49	39	**29**	**19**		

2. 70p; 50; 2

P100 **Assessment 4** 1. 10; 5 × 2/ 2 × 5; 2 + 2 + 2 + 2 + 2 = 10.

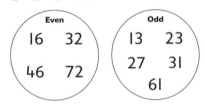

Spring Term

P103 **Solve it** 1. Answers will vary but check they total 10; 2. 5, 4, 3 or 2; 3. Answers will vary but check they total 8; 4. 4p, 3p, 2p, 1p.

P 105 **Where is it?** Check pictures have been correctly placed.

P107 **Assessment 5** (Strategies will vary, but check answers.) 1. 22; 2. 62; 3. 23; 4. 10.

P108 **Assessment 6** 1. 35; 2. 67; 3. 41

P111 **Opposite operations** Answers will vary.

P113 **Multiple dots** Check pairs correspond.

P115 **Assessment 7** Answers will vary but check the totals are correct.

P116 **Assessment 8** Answers will vary.

Answer sheet

Summer Term
P119 Up the hill Answers will vary.
P121 Made to measure Answers will vary.
P123 Assessment 9

1.

10	12	14	16	**18**	**20**	**22**	**24**
100	90	**80**	70	**60**	**50**	40	30
12	**15**	18	21	**24**	**27**	30	
45	40	**35**	**30**	25	20	**15**	
16	20	**24**	28	**32**	36		

2. 2, 14, 45, 50, 66, 82;
3. Answers will vary.

P124 Assessment 10 1. 60; 2. 30p
P127 Doubles and halves No answers.
P129 Multiplication triangles

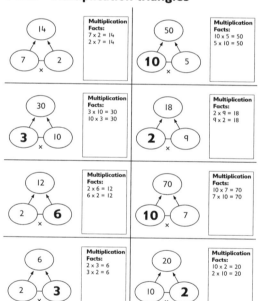

P131 Assessment 11 1. 3, 18, 27, 56, 95; 2.

a. **3** + 12 = 15
b. **15** – 12 = 3
c. **15** – 3 = 12
d. 15 – **3** = 12
e. 12 + **3** = 15

f. **20** – 4 = 16
g. **20** – 16 = 4
h. **4** + 16 = 20
i. 20 – **4** = 16
j. 4 + **16** = 20

P132 Assessment 12 1. a20; b16; c30; d26; e18; 2. a7; b10, c5, d3; e8; 3. Answers will vary.

P138 Check up 1 1. Answers will vary but check correct totals have been made;
2. 67, 77, 87;
3. 11, 11, 6, 17, 6;
4. 2 + 2 + 2 + 2 = 8

● ● ● ●
● ● ● ●

P139 Check up 2 5.

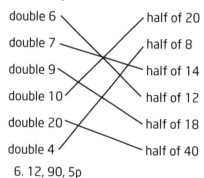

6. 12, 90, 5p

P140 Check up 3 7.

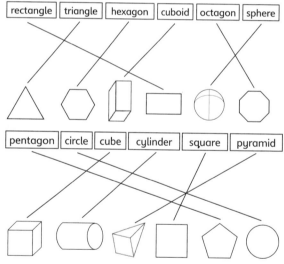

8. Check positional words are correctly assigned.